The Se

a natural history of the penis

by
Mels van Driel

Mandrake of Oxford

Published by
Mandrake of Oxford
PO Box 250
OXFORD
OX1 1AP (UK)

The Secret Part was published in the Netherlands as the best selling *Het Geheime Deel,* and is translated by Judith Abma-Hill

A CIP catalogue record for this book is available from the British Library and the US Library of Congress.

ISBN 1 869928 58X

Contents

vi Mels van Driel

Introduction

Everyone knows the feeling of being gripped by a certain subject. That never happens by coincidence. The subject attracts him or her like a magnet. After a while it can occupy that person day and night. New facts, ideas and thoughts press themselves forward time and time again. Now you are thinking, of course, that the writer is suffering from or has suffered from erectile disturbances. Not true, but you never know what might happen. This also applies to all male readers. The keen interest arises mainly from my daily contact with the 'secret part'.

I have been working within the field of urology since mid 1983. Meanwhile, thousands of penises have passed through my hands. And ultimately I realised that I wanted to find out more about this part of the anatomy. Why does a man consult a physician with complaints about 'him'?

Over the years a shaky balance has developed between urological, sexological and psychological view points, book-lore, the problems encountered at the impotence clinic, daily life and particularly the non-scientific literature. Writing with so many different hats on is not always easy, but it does offer a broader, more human perspective. It entails a sort of internal cross-fertilisation. Naturally, the novel literature always has the last word. Art comes before science. But for the urologist, the penis remains an organ, an organ that he or she (oh yes! there are female urologists in the Netherlands, about five out of the 250) cuts open to correct curvature, or to insert artificial inflatable cylinders into the corpora cavernosa.

Nearly all men feel that their penis is important. In the showers and changing rooms of sport facilities or elsewhere, open or secret inspections are made of another man's penis. If a man is given the choice of losing a hand or losing his genitals, then he will invariably choose the former. Losing a hand is a nuisance, but without penis and testicles a man is deeply humiliated. A well-formed member ranks as an expression of a powerful male personality. This is not only typical of humans. When the male of some species of ape thinks that he is facing a dangerous opponent, he uses an erect penis to command respect or to intimidate. This has nothing to do with sexuality in a narrow sense, but is chiefly the symbolisation of virility and strength. In our culture, it seems as though an erect penis is only associated with rape, destruction, oppression and banality. Perhaps this book can make a contribution to reviewing the meaning of the phallus. This does not alter the fact that banalities have to be discussed here and there. But that belongs to the penis as it were, not to the phallus.

The writing of this book has stemmed from a long succession of consultations with men who complained that 'he', whether or not temporarily, lay down on the job. Experience shows that the majority of these men think that their male identity depends purely on their capabilities in the sexual field. 'A man who cannot get an erection is not a man'. There is hardly any going back on this notion. The belief that sex stands or falls with coitus that leads to mutual orgasm is also tenacious.

The cause for a man's failure is very often psychological. In the course of the twentieth century, many psychological causes for impotence have therefore been given. These include for example, certain inhibitions which might have originated from his upbringing, too much concentration on work, on onanism, but the most important psychological factors remain fear of failure, anxiety about feelings of lust, in short, shrinking from sex in the broadest sense of the word. Quite correctly, the majority of sexologists agree that impotence is a far too complex problem to be left to urologists alone. Also from the point of view of other specialties, more attention is required for impotence, for example regarding the consequences of certain surgical interventions. In many men, removal of the prostate, bladder or rectum leads to impotence. Until recently, the treating physician did not usually mention this. The patient was expected to be pleased that his cancer had been cured. However, clinical practice has shown that it is wise to discuss these potential sexual problems before the operation. But this does not always happen. In the treatment of impotence, it is important to exclude as many physical causes as possible. But that too cannot always be adequately accomplished. In such a case the patient will have to rely on symptomatic therapies. These include:

♦ *'On demand' use of an oral drug (Viagra, Uprima, Yohimbine, Phentolamin).*
♦ *Intra-urethral administration of a pellet with a vasodilatory drug such as alprostadil (Muse) based on the discovery that the urethra (the normal pathway for urine) can absorb certain medications into the surrounding cavernous bodies, thereby creating an erection.*
♦ *The man injecting himself in the cavernous bodies of the penis with a vasodilatory drug (Caverject, Edex, Androskat, Viridal, Erecnos).*
♦ *Vacuum equipment that can start an erection by sucking in the blood, which is then kept in place by means of a ring.*
♦ *Surgical insertion of erection prostheses (AMS, Mentor), obviously an irreversible solution.*

These artificial solutions can also be useful in the treatment of psychogenic impotence, for example to break the vicious circle of impotence and fear of failure. Furthermore, certain men have rigid ideas about how things should happen in bed, which are not accessible to psychotherapy. Such men are better off with the urologists. It is important to realise that men with purely physical impotence, for instance after a rectal operation, sometimes feel a strong need to talk

- to a sexologist. On the other hand, some men with clear psychogenic impotence have great difficulty expressing their feelings and for that reason form suitable candidates for artificial solutions. Therefore, at the majority of university centres, urologists and sexologists work closely together.

This book also describes what many women think of an erect penis. Remarks made by feminist writers about male impotence are discussed extensively. In the seventies, people were convinced that there was a relationship between women's increased participation in society, the associated increase in female initiative in the sexual field and an increase in the occurrence of impotence. People wrote about 'new impotence'. In those days, the world was swamped with feminist confessional literature, in which humour and irony were usually very thinly sown. The approach to male impotence was rather brusque.

Luckily, second generation feminists, such as Renate Dorrestein and Yvonne Kroonenberg, approached the problem in a different more humoristic manner. These women present impotence in such a way that what they write can pass as sex therapy! Other authors do the same with premature ejaculation. The latter is a poignant and also very common problem. It is a generally known fact that three out of four men reach orgasm within two minutes of starting coitus. Some individuals even do that before the penis has penetrated the vagina. Are there solutions for this? The book provides information about that, too.

Smelling and Feeling

In the last chapter, it is emphasized that better cooperation between sexologists and urologists will undoubtedly be of great benefit to men with erectile problems. A sexologist will, for example, make it clear to his colleague that for many men, coitus is the only way that they can *feel* love for their wife. But at the same time, they have to be convinced that they are satisfying her. Biologists believe that it is important for a woman to have an orgasm about once a month, because when a woman becomes sexually aroused, she produces *pheromones*, aromatic substances. During a female orgasm, a hundred times more of these substances are produced than under normal conditions. Men should be able to smell these substances as it were, in order to become aroused themselves. However, this does not happen all by itself. People also need pubic hair, which is meant to retain these aromatic substances. If his partner has not reached an orgasm in a long time, then a man will gradually lose interest in her. Therefore, impotence usually has both psychological and physical causes.

Under certain circumstances, no therapy - accepting a man's impotence- takes preference. Because when the doubts about potency ultimately fade away, there will be a great deal more time for magnificent walks, long discussions beside the open fire and visits to the theatre or exhibitions. Older couples often decide after many years to end their sexual activities and find that they can spend their time in better ways. After all, married life consists of more than an erection!

Who is this book meant for? Obviously, chiefly for men who have at least passed the age of forty years. In order to be able to muse beside the open fire on earlier conquests and pleasant sexual experiences ('le cinéma erotique intérieure'), on their failures, and death. The book is also meant for women, however, whether or not disappointed in their past sexual life. The tone is elegant and here and there jestful, the best way to greet decay, impotence and death.

List of Illustrations

1
About the secret part

According to modern insights, erection of the penis depends on the correct hormone balance, a healthy anatomy, adequate blood supply and an undamaged, well-functioning nervous system. He or she who lets this sink in deeply will realise that things are likely to go wrong sometimes; to go one better, it is a miracle that an erection goes well so often! Obviously, the same applies to ejaculation.

'Impotence' means literally 'wholly lacking in sexual power'. The word is often used in a belittling sense to insinuate helplessness. Probably, impotence is one of the best kept bedroom secrets. In any case, for the person suffering from it, it is one of the most shameful.

In the past, doctors distinguished between different forms of impotence:*impotentia erigendi, impotentia ejaculandi* and*impotentia generandi*. This book chiefly deals with the former, namely the incapacity to have an erection that lasts long enough for coitus. In men with *impotentia ejaculandi*, there is no problem with having an erection and penetrating the vagina, but they are unable to reach orgasm and ejaculate. In general, this is not possible by masturbation either. It is a fairly uncommon complaint.

Impotentia generandi means the incapacity to reproduce. It is a question of male infertility and can be viewed as a form of social impotence. Strikingly, you often hear in everyday conversations 'she can't have any children', or 'they can't have any children', but you hardly ever hear 'he is infertile', or 'he cannot father any children'. Apparently that is too painful.

It is not customary to display an erection or to copulate in public. In fact, such behaviour is punishable by law. In order to be able to demonstrate that a man is nevertheless functioning adequately, there is only one possibility left, namely for him to father a child. If this is not possible because of poor sperm quality, then the man involved feels that he is severely lacking. At present, the situation is somewhat easier, because quite a few couples choose not to have children.

There has never been an impotent woman. Apart from rare anatomical or psychological abnormalities, every woman can have sexual intercourse by passively accepting the sexual advances of a man. According to western standards, this does not apply to men. In ancient China, people also propagandized 'soft' penetration, in other words, with a flaccid penis. More about that later. The relationship between a man and his penis cannot therefore be compared to that between a woman and her clitoris and/or vagina. A woman can say, 'I don't feel like it'. For her, the vagina is an integral part of her body. Obviously, the penis is the same for a man too, but an erect penis, the phallus, is much more.

In the novel *The Two of Us* by the Italian author Alberto Moravia, the hero Frederico is forever experiencing problems with his enormous and highly demanding phallus, which he calls Rex. It is a shatteringly candid book, in which the central figure has continual conversations with his 'rebellious' member that does not shrink from any erotic slip-up. The story ends with a humiliating scene for Frederico, in which his member -'he'- demands that he goes to see his wife although they are having a year's trial separation and also bawls to be 'set free' (with which Frederico complies) in the lift on the way up to her flat:

To satisfy him. I pressed the bell once more. Standing stiffly in the air, 'he' seemed now to be rising up, in short, successive jerks, as

if to bring himself to the level of the keyhole and look into the flat.
At last I heard a slight bustling sound. Then Fausta's voice asking:
'Who is it?'
'It's me, Rico.'
Fausta's hand undid the chain, the door opened, and she appeared
on the threshold in her dressing-gown. She looked at me, looked
down, saw 'him' and then, without saying a word, put out her hand
to take hold of 'him', as one might take hold of a donkey's halter to
make it move. Then she turned her back to me, pulling 'him' in
behind her, and, with 'him', me. She went into the flat; 'he' went
behind her; I followed them both.

The title of the novel is very appropriate. Many men are under the impression or think that their penis has a sort of *own will* and does whatever **it** wants to. Quite a few men therefore speak just like Frederico about 'him' when they are referring to their penis. 'He' is a symbol of the capacity to reproduce with the associated feelings of male self-respect. Muscular strength, determination, effectiveness, penetration, directness, power - the phallus lies at the root of all of these.

However, sooner or later every man comes to realise that his penis is not like an arm, finger or leg. The penis does not perform on command. It can be compared with a well-trained dog, which usually carries out the assignments given, but the master should always bear in mind that he might be let down now and then, despite the fact that the dog has been well-trained, or in human terms, socialised. Men can gain some 'control' over their penis. On a nudist beach for instance, you hardly ever see men with erections, while everywhere there are naked women (and men) to admire. And a woman with her legs in the stirrups of an examination table to undergo cystoscopy, will not cause an erection in a single urologist. He addresses himself to one specific part of the body of the woman who is ill.

The Phallus

'Phallus' is the name for an erect penis as a symbol. The majority of people associate the notion 'penis' with something or someone else, for example their bearded biology teacher from the sixties or books by doctors about sex education. That is not to say that these were bad textbooks. On the contrary, for the pubertal boy, at least something of the *secret parts* of his penis remain intact. Modern sex education books are very intrusive and leave little to the imagination. What is nicer during puberty than to discover things for yourself and learn to make your own judgements? Fortunately, for the majority of children discovering the difference between male and female external genitals is still a very exciting experience. Who has never played doctors and nurses? At that age, the differences are discussed extensively, but most adults no longer do that or dare to. In his fascinating novel *Het jaar van de kreeft* (Cancer year), the Flemish author Hugo Claus describes such a discovery.

> *'You have got the nicest little cunt that I have ever seen', he whispered.*
> *'No', she said. 'It used to be nice. But after I had the baby, they stitched me up all wrong. And then I started suffering from piles. It often hurts a lot.'*
> *'I love you', said Pierre.*
> *'I love you, too', she answered. 'And you've also got the nicest one I've ever seen. I don't usually look at it in men'.*
> *'But if you didn't look, how do you know that mine's nicer?'*
> *'Well, I might have had a sneaky look. They are usually red or blueish, with all those horrible veins. Ugh.-'*

This passage shows what most women think of the penis. The phallus, the erect penis, enjoys a completely different reputation. In many old cultures, the phallus was the symbol of immortality, of eternal rejuvenated life. The Etruscans placed a phallus on every grave. As externally visible biological characteristic, the phallus has received a heavy religious and moral load in the course of history. No matter what, studying the phallus always leads us beyond the religious sciences. The phallus rises up, and as one who is 'immortal', can repeat this masterpiece time and time again. The repetitive*resurrection of the flesh* in optimal form.

The phallus culture was a striking feature in the religion of the ancient Greeks. An impotent man received more scorn than sympathy. A small phallus was preferred by the Greeks. A large one was associated with barbarians and satyrs. This may be related to the notion of Aristotle that a shorter penis would increase fertility. According to him 'the sperm cooled down less when the distance it had to travel was shorter'. Centuries later, evolutionary biologists claimed the opposite: a longer penis promotes fertility!

Herms stood 'everywhere' in ancient Greece, not only in front of houses, but also by temples and city gates, in front of castles, at markets and in gymnasia. These squared pillars with only a male head on top and a phallus that stuck out in front were crowned with green branches and wetted with olive oil. During worship, people placed their hand on the herm's head, took hold of his beard and his phallus. This could not be done in public nowadays. At the *Piazza della signora* in Florence, there is a statue of Neptune in the middle of an ornamental pond, with bronze fauns sitting around the edge. The naked fauns all have a penis in erection. Whereas the bronze of the fauns shows the usual oxidation colour, the phalluses are yellow-copper coloured, owing to the uncountable touching of hands. Florentine women believe that in this way they can increase their chance of pregnancy. But while the touching takes place in secret in Florence, it occurred without scruples and openly in ancient Greece.

The symbolic meaning of the phallus is much more than just sexual. Dionysian festivals illustrated the religious meaning of the phallus. Large phalluses were carried in the processions. Dionysus was the god of intoxication, of the exaltation caused by wine, the blood of the earth. He was the god of passion, enthusiasm, the god of blatant abandonment, which characterised these nocturnal autumn festivals.

In *Acharnen*, the Greek philosopher Aristophanes describes the procession during the private Dionysian festival at which the good man Dikaiopolis celebrates the occasion of the peace between Athens and Sparta with his daughter and their slave Xanthios. Dikaiopolis orders Xanthios to hold the phallus stick out in front of him and then sings the following phallic hymn:

> *Oh, Phales, companion of Bacchus,*
> *leader of parties, old goat,*
> *lover of women and boys,*
> *with peace in my hands I greet you*
> *and jubilant I return to my home.*

The enormous city festivals were important state occasions. They were celebrated with great pomp and circumstance and attracted onlookers from miles around. Not only were countless phallus images were carried in the procession, but the participants also tied large artificial penises to themselves.

Apart from this, it was the Greeks in particular who drew a sharp dividing line between the phallus with its symbolic meaning and the same organ as an anatomical part. The phallus was only used symbolically and in rituals.

An Egyptian story of the Creation tells about the god Atum, who created the world by standing in the primaeval sea and masturbating. From his phallus he spewed Shu and Tefnet, air and water, brother and sister, and thus creation was a fact.

A phallus is also described in the Hindu story of the Creation. On the day of their creation, when the gods Brahma and Vishnu appeared from nothing, they were bewildered, but 'presently they saw a magnificent *Lingam* of gigantic proportions, whose ends reached unmeasurably far'.

Also within the religion of other ancient peoples, the phallus played an important role. Not only within the Baal religion (Baal was the phallic god of the Moabites), but also within Islam and Judaism, circumcision of the foreskin formed a sign of covenant between the man and Baal, Allah or Jahweh..

It is worth mentioning that in Bible, *Deuteronomy* chapter 23, which is about who is forbidden to enter into the congregation of the Lord, it says 'he that is wounded in the stones, or hath his privy member cut off'.

According to the etymologist Scott, the Bible translators consciously replaced the word 'penis' by the obscure word 'hip'. For example, in Genesis 24 verse 2, Abraham says to his servant: 'Put your hand under my hip, because I swear by almighty God of heaven and earth that [...].' In Abraham's time, it was customary when one swore to God for a man to put his hand against his own penis or against that of the person whom it was all about. There was nothing special about that. A circumcised penis was the sign of the covenant between men and Jahweh.

Within Christianity, the penis has gradually sunk into the background as a religious symbol, although according to legend, particularly in France, certain holy men were attributed powers of healing for impotence until the end of last century. People in need could address themselves to these holy men.

Until 1805, when the village of Iserna near Naples was hit by an earthquake, a picturesque pilgrimage took place each year on 17 September. At the local cathedral, relics of Saint Damien were stored. You can probably guess which. On the big day, these were carried in the procession which ended up at the local fair. Phalluses made of wax in all sorts of shapes and sizes were sold there. While saying a certain prayer, they could be hung up in the chapel. The proceeds naturally went to the church.

Phallus worship was sanctioned within the Catholic church at a few other places. Details can be found about them in *A history of phallic worship* by Knight and Wright. In general, the Church of Rome did not encourage phallus worship. However, this did not alter the fact that until 1913, anyone who was chosen by the conclave of cardinals to mount the throne of Saint Peter, first had to be felt from beneath. Every Roman Catholic knows that there is a large hole in the seat of the Holy

Chair. On balance, it was not unknown for the gentlemen to have been mistaken. In 855 they had mistakenly chosen a certain lady named Johanna. That could not be tolerated a second time. When one of the cardinals had established that the prospective Pope was *male* through the hole in the chair, he spoke the words, 'Testiculos habet et bene pedentes'. After the above-mentioned error, candidate monks, just like the pope, were examined carefully for body parts that they would subsequently never be allowed to use!

Other names

In the ancient Greek and Latin languages, there was already a wide variety of names for the male genital organ. Only a few have been preserved. It is often difficult to discover why one name continued to be used, while another did not. The majority of words were metaphors related to length, cylindrical shape or vertical position. Sometimes the stem of a plant, the shaft of a spear or the blade of a sword served as a model, or sometimes the vertical warp of fabric (Greek *stêma*), or the bronze beak of a war-galley that was intended to ram other ships during sea battles (Greek *embolon*). The classicists Horstmanshof and Beukers made a study of this topic. The accepted anatomical name for the female genital organ, 'vagina' (sheath), links up beautifully with the blade of a sword. The same applies to the term 'ejaculation' (seminal discharge, derived from the Latin *iaculum*, 'small spear') with the shaft of a spear. Ejaculation is therefore the flinging away of sperm, as a spear.

Ultimately, it became 'penis'. The precise origin of 'penis' remains unclear. Some language experts believed that the word was derived from the Latin verb 'pendere' (to hang). In that case the vulgar Dutch noun 'lul' is not such a bad translation, because the verb 'lullen' originally meant 'hanging down'. The status of words that originally had a neutral meaning can rise and fall on account of all sorts of factors, from obscene to scientific, and from decent and descriptive to vulgar. Another such Dutch word is 'kloot' (ball/testicle), which was used by the Dutch poet Joost van den Vondel in literary language, but is used almost exclusively today as a vulgar expression (±bastard).

'Penis' has therefore gone far in the world. A Dutchman who wishes to avoid three-letter words (equivalent to four-letter words in English) will undoubtedly seek refuge in the scientific designation. After all, there are not many alternatives. Except for the Dutch homosexual author Gerard Reve, hardly anybody uses the archaic word 'roede' (rod). According to the two above-mentioned classicists, this is a sister word for the German *Ruthe*, the French *verge* and the English *mansyard*. These are all translations of the Arabic *al-kamarah*. This word was used in the ancient influential Arabian medical literature. Via Latin (*virga*, 'twig', 'sprig') has been adopted in western European languages.

In Sanskrit, completely different metaphors were used for the male member. *De tuin der lusten* (*The Garden of Lusts*) by Sheik Nefzwai, includes the following:

- *the 'dove', because the moment an erect member starts to go limp it looks like a dove sitting on her eggs;*
- *the 'jingler' / 'rattler' because every time the member goes in and out of the vagina it makes a noise;*
- *the 'untamable', because as soon as it is in erection, it goes into action and continues to search for the entrance to the vulva until it finds it, and then forces its way in with not so much as a by your leave;*
- *the 'liberator', because by entering the vulva of a woman who has been repudiated three times, it gives the woman freedom to return to her first husband;*
- *the 'rod', because the member slowly creeps upwards between a woman's thighs to her mount of Venus, subsequently approaches the entrance to the vulva, and then slips inside, until it has nestled there pleasurably and ejaculated;*
- *the 'crowbar', because the member, if the vulva is too tight, forces its way in as it were and in the process breaks and tramples everything around it, just like a wild animal in rut;*

- *'baldy', because a member does not have a hair on its head!*

According to the Dutchman of letters Hans van Straten, in the Middle Ages people called the penis *caulis*, or 'stem'. Other commonly used names at that time were among others: thing, mast, point, reed, staff, piece, udder, finch, whistle, spout, stalk, bird, sausage, bobber, rifle, jewel, clapper, mouse, bush, key, soldier, clarinet, rose tree, cinnamon stick, plaything, flesh arrow, instrument, love weapon, thermometer, wag-in-front, little man, trombone, Venus priest, women's comforter, little Ferdinand and Lady Venus hunter. In comparison, these days we have a very limited vocabulary.

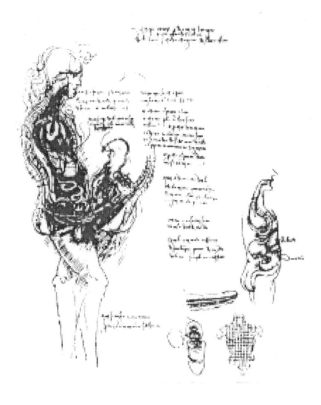

Figure 1: Leonardo Da Vinci's view of coitus and erection (1494)

The beginnings of science

One of the first people to study the penis scientifically was Leonardo Da Vinci (1452-1519). Thus, the most inspired mind known to world history was also interested in the genital organs. According to him, not only the male genital organs but also those of the female were so repulsive that if the beauty of the human body as a whole did not exist and there were no irrepressible sexual desires, mankind would have died out long ago. Through his anatomical studies, Da Vinci fell into conflict with the prohibition against performing autopsies on the deceased.

This brilliant man - with an erotic preference for the male sex - refuted the medieval idea that an erection was brought about by the accumulation of air. By studying criminals who had died on the gallows, he concluded that it occurred through the accumulation of blood. This applies to all mammals. In birds on the contrary, an erection is the result of lymph congestion. However, the large majority of birds do not actually have a penis, in other words an organ with *corpora cavernosa*. Only the *Ratites* - which includes for example the ostrich - and the *Anseres* - swans, geese and ducks that copulate underwater- have a sort of penis with erectile tissue.

The anatomist Varolio (1543-1575) published reports on the penis several decades after Da Vinci. His most important conclusion was that the muscles on the underside play a major role in an erection. Modern insights agree with this. These muscles make the penis extra stiff. Reinier de Graaf (1641-1673) a world-famous Dutch scientist, invented a sort of syringe that he used to study the deceased. When he injected water into the hypogastric artery - in one of his subjects, to his surprise the cavernous bodies of the penis filled up. He confirmed the conclusion of his colleague Varolio. It was not until 1863 that Eckhardt from Germany demonstrated that stimulating the sacral part of the spinal cord could cause an erection. The erection centre was situated in the lowest part of the spinal cord. It took many years until more became known about penile erection.

Equipment to record the presence of - nocturnal and erotic -

erections was sold for the first time at the end of the nineteenth century. Not for application to humans, but for stud stallions. Horse breeders know from time immemorial that these animals tend to masturbate instead of waiting for a willing mare. As masturbation decreases the sperm quality, the penis was hung in a sort of net with bells attached to it. Whenever the stallion had an erection, the bells would ring and the horse breeder could intervene. It was sold for eight dollars, a considerable sum of money in those days.

In the nineteen-forties, German scientists discovered that not only adult men, but also male babies could have nightly erections. Apparently these nocturnal erections were not associated with high testosterone levels, as these do not start to rise until puberty. In the fifties, equipment was designed to measure erections 'objectively'. Naturally, misuse followed. In Czechoslovakia the equipment was used to unmask young men who, in order to be excluded from national service, claimed to be homosexual. While wearing an erection-meter, the recruits were given hard hetero-pornography to look at, which soon found them out!

The erection-meter was still being used in England in the nineties, for the psychiatric assessment of prisoners serving long-term sentences for sexual crimes. Prison psychiatrists showed their patients perverse or violent videos and the sensors in the collars fitted around the penis registered whether or not the patient still became aroused. If a patient became aroused, he was not yet ready for society. These examples show that the medical profession is all too eager to conduct perversions of the government.

Sometimes it is the patient himself who insists on having nightly erection measurements. An example is a forty-two year old man who was accused of having sexual relations with his stepdaughter. The lawcourts had already sentenced him to months of imprisonment. He declared to his lawyer and his general practitioner that he had been suffering from impotence for many years and therefore could not be guilty. He wanted to have this confirmed and was subsequently admitted for a short while for erection measurements. These appeared to be normal. He had little more to say.

Masturbation

Masturbation is defined as the activity by which, through manipulation of their own sexual organ, a person causes his/her own sexual arousal and possible orgasm. Other names are self-gratification and onanism. The word masturbation is derived from Latin *manus* ('hand') and *stuprare* ('violation', 'rape'). Translated literally thus, it receives the absurd meaning: raping oneself with one's own hand. In practice, we mean the phenomenon that humans and animals of all ages and of either sex, under certain circumstances and through certain manipulations, are capable of putting themselves into a state of sexual

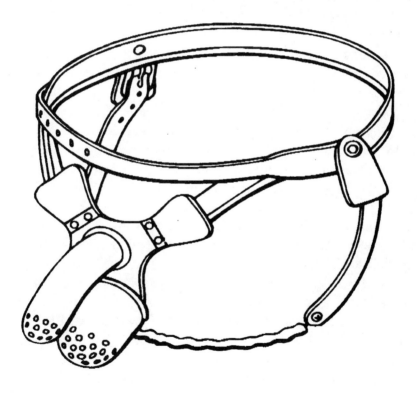

Figure 2: A night-time harness to prevent masturbation

arousal.

At the end of the nineteenth century, physicians believed that impotence was the result of sexual excesses or excessive masturbation:

> *The onanist cannot accomplish coitus, his member has lost its give, its ability to rise. The noble fluid, his strength, his male value, his beauty, is lost. The source from which surged energy, will-power, courage and pride, talent and pleasure, has dried up, all of this has been recklessly wasted; perhaps something has remained, but what little there is, however, is thin, watery, powerless and moreover flows too quickly.*

So said an anonymous physician in those days, quoted in De Vries' *Ha dokter, ho dokter* (*Ah Doctor, Oh Doctor*). The foundation of this line of reasoning was the scarcity theory. To guard boys against an erection or masturbation, so-called penis rings were applied before they went to bed at night. These metal rings could only just be slipped over the flaccid penis. Sharp serrated teeth were attached to the inside. Erection immediately led to severe pain. Penile harnesses were also used. A few decades later, this somatic interpretation of masturbation faded into the background through the emergence of psychoanalysis.

For the reader who did not receive a pious upbringing: the name 'onanism' is incorrectly derived from Onan, a grandson of Father Jacob. According to ancient Jewish custom, Onan's father demanded that he marry Tamar his brother's widow who had remained childless, and give her children. Onan did not want to and 'therefore, whenever he came to his brother's wife, wasted his seed on the ground, so as not to give his brother offspring' (Genesis 38:19). We presently call Onan's behaviour coitus interruptus.

William Alexander Hammond (1828-1900), surgeon and later professor of nerve and nervous diseases in New York, was convinced that masturbation, especially at a young age, was the most important cause for the absence of erection. In the second chapter of his book *Het sexueel onvermogen bij den man en bij den vrouw* (Sexual Impotence in Men and Women), published in the Netherlands in 1891, Hammond covers more than one hundred pages with his conviction of the ins and outs of the matter. According to him, organs must be ripe before they can be utilised. If a child is forced to study at a young age, he or she is in serious danger of developing epilepsy or of becoming a dunce. Heavy physical labour would stunt the child's growth and make him or her backward or weak. Hammond therefore firmly believed that stimulation of the genital organs at an 'unripe' age would lead to impotence:

> *In very young children it sometimes happens that petting in order to make them quiet involves stroking their genitals and in that way sensations are created that are pleasurable, and which they seek later. In some cases, the child copies the action, and if this practice is continued until after puberty, total impotence occurs through loss of male capability and often also through lack of desire.*

As a warning, the professor tells the story of a young shepherd who had already turned to onanism at a young age. Ultimately, one thing and another led to horrible complications:

> *The shepherd surrendered himself to onanism at the age of fifteen years and did it up to fifteen times a day. He went so far that ejaculation followed only seldom and sometimes required an effort of one hour long. Sometimes he was racked by convulsions while performing onanism and deposited a few drops of blood instead of sperm. For eleven years he only used his hand, but in about his twenty-sixth year, because he could no longer achieve the usual sensations by this means, he took refuge in another means and that was to stick a rod of about eight inches long into his urethra several times per day. He continued to do this for sixteen years, but ultimately the mucous membrane of his urethra became hard, calloused and numb: the rod no longer achieved the aim it was meant to; he had become the victim of a persistent erection, which*

could not be assuaged by anything.

The whole time, the shepherd had an aversion to women. He became melancholy, neglected his work and ended up only trying to satisfy his lusts. One day he used a knife to make an incision right across his glans, parallel with the urethra. This operation gave him pleasurable sensations and led to an abundant ejaculation. After having repeated this horrible mutilation a number of times, the unfortunate shepherd noticed that he had cleaved his penis in two, from the urethral opening to his pubic bone. Hammond recounts this illustratively:

> *When the bleeding became too profuse, he arrested it by tying a piece of string around his member. The spongy bodies, although separated, were still capable of erection, but deviated to the left and right. Once the member was cleaved right up to the pubic bone, the knife was no longer necessary.*

New attempts and new disappointments followed:

> *He took a shorter rod than he had used up till then and stuck it into what remained of his urethra. He thus managed to stimulate the openings of the seed canals and achieve ejaculation.*
>
> *For ten years he gratified himself in this manner, until one day through carelessness it slipped through his fingers and slid into his bladder. He instantly felt severe pain and all his attempts to remove the foreign body were fruitless.*
>
> *In the end, after suffering severely through the congestion of urine and contusions in the bladder, he consulted a surgeon, who was obviously very surprised to find two members instead of one, each of which the size of the original member. The severity of the pain caused the surgeon to decide on the stone incision, as a result of which he was able to produce a rod, that after having remained in the bladder for three months, was covered in a chalky substance.*

After severe collapses, the patient recovered from the operation, but died three months later from tuberculosis, which had been caused by his manifold and persistent excesses.

After reading this story you might think that such things do not happen nowadays. Well then, every experienced urologist will have encountered at least one patient who, in all his loneliness, has tried to obtain sexual satisfaction with an electricity lead or something equivalent. Such experiments often come to an end in a chilly operating theatre.

Not only adolescents, but also elderly men became Hammond's targets.

... many men who are impotent in their attempts at intercourse, not through lack of lust, but through lack of strength, systematically turn to onanism, by which means ejaculation and satisfaction without erection can be achieved, very much to the detriment of their genital instincts and potency.

Elderly men sometimes take refuge in the same means, whose natural lust and potency are weakened, but who through one type of lecherous practice or another, or even by losing themselves in lecherous thoughts, can reawaken them. These cases belong to the most deplorable that one might meet, especially if the deed is often repeated, and under circumstances that cause various after-effects, such as epilepsy or stroke. I chanced upon the case of an elderly man of 73 years who received two young girls every afternoon for the purpose of fellatio one after the other with hardly a quarter of an hour between.

One day he suddenly became paralysed and could no longer speak: a blood vessel in one side of his brain had burst.
In another case an over 70-year-old suffered paralytic tremors, probably caused by sclerosis (sickly hardening of the brain tissues) which was a clear consequence of his exceptional habit of onanism carried out over several years. In this case the sexual urges were

abnormally stimulated by obscene literature and pictures, and although he never had an erection, he successfully achieved a state of over-sensitivity through excessive incitement, which led to satisfaction and weak ejaculation.

One day when he was busy gratifying himself, he noticed slight dizziness and his right hand immediately started to tremble. The trembling became stronger and started to affect his other hand, his head and his throat. Both legs became affected soon afterwards, and now he is swiftly reverting to a child-like state.

Nevertheless these stories are not intended to mean that masturbation is an unhealthy form of sex. On the contrary, according to modern beliefs, masturbation is a form of sperm quality control. It can never become old and stale. A popular American professor said to his students once that masturbation has many much-needed advantages: it saves time and money, it avoids any unpleasant relationships and obligations, it does not make anybody unhappy and there is no risk of catching infectious diseases; but on the other hand, it is not advisable to do it five times in quick succession. The seminal vesicles become empty and towards the end, only a little reddish yellow fluid appears, or in the worse case, a few drops of blood.

Ronald Giphart is a very popular writer in Dutch student circles. He concludes his novel *Giph* with a few wild ideas about masturbation:

I was sitting naked on the toilet seat rubbing my stomach and feeling so sorry for myself (really) that I almost had an erection. Look at that, he is already growing, 'my little man'. Yes, let's talk about that [..].

I looked at it, at my prick. 'I want to tell you something important', I whispered to him. 'Feel the energy in my moving hand flowing through you. I thought: Imagine that at this very moment, now, unexpectedly, Vesuvius has an enormous eruption and the whole of Europe becomes covered in lava, and that I get preserved in my present state, and after many centuries American researchers

come along and find me and hack me out and then put me in an
archaeological museum, in a backroom, and I will 'live on' with the
wicked label: Desperately Masturbating Adolescent'.

In these enlightened times, even an anthology of poems about masturbation has been published, compiled by Rob Schouten. *Met de hand* (Manually) is the title and it contains among others a sonnet 'Op Gijsen' by Gerrit Komrij. In the first quatrain the poet approaches the subject with little subtlety:

I weep for priests, stuck in gowns,
While god's fluid grows in their loins,
I weep for acorns (glans), that are always inflamed,
And for their hands that should go up and down.

Urologists

Within the world of urology, it is thought that meddling with impotence is something completely new. This is a misconception based on ignorance about history. Even before the turn of the century, there were a few Dutch 'urologists' interested in male impotence. At that time there was no official register for urologists. In 1898, a doctor called Van der Spek published an article on this subject in the *Medisch Weekblad voor Noord - en Zuid-Nederland* (Medical Weekly for North and South Holland). An excerpt:

In this material, the 'Harnröhren specialists' do not have the monopoly. But they may also have their say, even for the only reason that the majority of impotents turn to them for advice. In this way, these specialists automatically pay attention to this part of medical science. They will learn quickly that the majority of impotents are very pitiable individuals, who deserve better fortune than to fall into the hands of unscrupulous charlatans, which happens all too often. In many cases impotence is a pitiful complaint.

Very often it is better to be dead than impotent. A person with untimely impotence belongs to the most unhappy of creatures; and his misery is so much greater because he believes that he has to feel ashamed, believes that he has to conceal it; he is the target of mockery and very seldom receives sympathy.

The way in which we must try to heal him cannot be described in a few words.

For a start, sexual abstinence must be demanded from the patient. Multiple pollutions must be avoided as much as possible. Short periods of sleep, in the prone position, a hard bed, not too many covers, light evening meal, avoidance of all possible sexual stimulation, are the first to be advised.

It is desirable to undergo treatment at hospital, where in many cases a course of treatment with horse manure can be applied that has extremely good results. In the meantime a very experienced doctor must give the necessary instructions for the treatment, because it is often useful to alternate rest with moderate mental and physical work. Attention must also be paid to over-eating, massage, electricity, etc., according to the circumstances.

But not all patients can be admitted for observation. If not, then in many cases, most can be expected of electrical treatment. As a rule it is best to use constant current and to place the anode between the shoulder blades and the cathode in the crutch, and then to place the anode on the lumbar spine and the cathode alternately on spermatic cords, penis and perineum.

In his article the physician indicates that a great deal of physical exercise might free an impotent man from his complaint. However, he advises against horse riding and cycling. At that time too, it was apparently evident that a poorly fitting saddle could lead to pins and needles and sometimes to a loss of feeling in the penis. Persistent pressure on the urethra during an extremely long cycle ride can lead to the glans remaining completely flaccid during a subsequent erection.

Such numbness of the penis can be explained by long-term pressure on the nerves that supply the area between the testicles and anus. The function of these nerves is temporarily restricted. Fortunately, the numbness usually disappears spontaneously after a while.

Testosterone

Almost two thousand years ago, the Greek physician Plinius recommended eating goat's testicles to treat inadequate sexual functioning. In many countries, testes can be found on the menu. In Spain, this delicacy is known as *Cojones*. This is the Spanish word for 'courageous'. It is an illusion to think that a man's testosterone level can be increased in this way. Just about everything left in the testes will go down the drain. Any tiny amounts of testosterone that are absorbed by the intestines will be broken down directly by the liver.

In the eighteenth century, the English surgeon John Hunter (1728-1793) performed some very important and original work. He was the first to observe that the testes of animals slaughtered in the autumn were smaller than those of animals slaughtered in the spring. The reason why became apparent only recently. Under the influence of long periods of sunlight, the pineal gland at the base of the brain produces more melatonin, which stimulates hormone production in the pituitary gland. In turn, the pituitary gland stimulates the tests to produce larger quantities of testosterone and sperm.

Hunter also performed experiments on animals. After he had transplanted a piece of testicle from a cockerel into a hen, the hen became masculinized. She developed a cockscomb. Unfortunately, Hunter forgot to publish many of his findings. Consequently, his name is missing from the majority of books about medical history.

Around the year 1900, the average life expectancy increased noticeably. Better nutrition and hygiene were chiefly responsible for this. A steadily increasing number of people reached at least middle age. More or less in agreement with the present juncture, many people in la belle époque felt the need to resist the ravages of old age. It has been known since Roman times from the observation of eunuchs, that male potency is related to the testicles, but around the turn of the

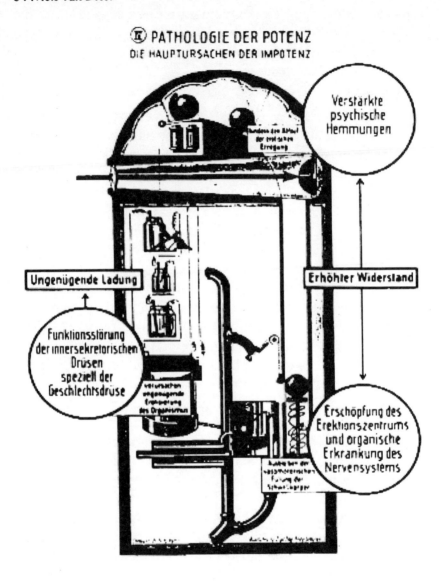

Figure 3: Disrupted potency, explained with the aid of cylinders, springs, valves, rods, pumps and Maagdenburger half-spheres

century, people believed that *vitality* was also connected with the testicles.

A young Viennese physiologist, Eugen Steinach, assumed that 'youth' was brought about by the puberty glands, the testicles. In the elderly, testicular function might lead to a second youth. This was not an original thought, because the famous physiologist, Edouard Brown-Sequard (1817-1894) had already ventilated such ideas. However, these were jeered at by his colleague researchers, because he had treated himself with subcutaneous injections of extracts from canine testicles and had dared to declare it in public.

In 1912 Steinach started a series of experiments on old rats. The animals had poor skin, were scrawny and no longer had any desire for sex. Their seminal vesicles were thought to be flaccid and empty, which prompted Steinach to tie off their spermatic ducts, including the efferent blood vessels. He expected that this would increase the blood supply to the testicles, with a proportional increase in testosterone production.

According to tradition, his male rats proved him right. They grew more hair, became more alert, more aggressive and their sexual interest returned. The rats that did not show the expected result had the testicles of young rats implanted into their abdomen or abdominal wall. This led to some degree of improvement. The rats lived a year longer than their generally allotted life expectancy of three years.

On 1 November 1918, the time was ripe. An exhausted, emaciated and apathetic Viennese labourer was the first person to undergo bilateral tying-off of the spermatic ducts. In the first two months after the operation, little changed. A short while later he started to pick up, eat better, develop bulkier muscles and was able to return to work. As reborn, this crown witness of the rejuvenation operation wandered through the streets of Vienna! Elderly gentlemen with sufficient money soon found surgeons who were prepared to perform this operation on them.

Currently, tying off the spermatic ducts (and removing a small portion: vasectomy) is the most practical method of becoming infertile.

On the basis of a recent survey among Dutch urologists, it can be estimated that between thirty and forty thousand men are sterilised per year. The national databank network of general practitioners shows that in the period 1972-1991, at least 701,500 men were 'seen to'. On the basis of this data it can be estimated that about 12% of Dutchmen have been sterilised. As far as we know, Holland is the only country in the world where more men than women (about nine per cent) have been sterilised. In addition, about three to four hundred reversal operations take place in Holland; in other words, one per cent of men who have been sterilised wish to have the situation reversed. The number of men who are *sorry* that they underwent the intervention is much larger, about 3%. One reason might be that they feel a dragging pain during ejaculation.

Back to history. Steinach was considered to be a charlatan by many of his colleagues. He was well aware of the limitations of his experiments, because the research area of ageing, impotence and possible hormonal influences was much too complicated for one single poverty-stricken scientist. He hoped that others would continue his work.

In Paris in the same period, Serge Voronoff started to create a furore with testicular extracts. After diverse wanderings through Africa, this eccentric, flamboyant Russian became head of the - at that time - famous experimental laboratory of the Collège de France. As a surgeon in Algeria, he had become interested in the fate of castrated boys. He found them to be psychologically and physically retarded. It was usual practice at that time for patients with tuberculosis of the genitals to undergo castration. Tuberculosis was a very common bacteriological disease in those days, which chiefly affected the lungs, but could also spread to the kidneys and genital organs. In Voronoff's opinion this would lead to loss of memory and concentration within a few years. Moreover, he had never seen a eunuch of older than sixty years of age. Consequently, he assumed that losing the testicles accelerated the ageing process. He was convinced that old testicles required assistance. Unfortunately, Steinach's operation (tying off the spermatic ducts) ultimately produced far too few satisfied patients. In addition, Voronoff had become convinced through his experiments on rats that transplanting young testicles under the skin of the abdomen did not help either. Without an adequate blood supply, the testicular tissue soon perished. Vascular surgery had not yet made sufficient advances. These days, even tiny blood vessels can be stitched together with the aid of a microscope.

Voronoff subsequently decided to approach the matter in a different manner from his Viennese colleague. He took testicular tissue, cut it into thin slices and transplanted it into the membranous capsule of the existing testicles. He then scored the capsule with his scalpel, in the hope that this would stimulate the growth of new blood vessels to supply the graft. The most spectacular part was the donor. Whereas the followers of Steinach had used undescended testicles from young men, Voronoff used apes' testicles.

In June 1920, he performed his first transplant. By 1923, the Russian had personally performed forty-three operations, half of which on patients younger than sixty years. These were obviously not poor folk. They included professors, architects, writers and industrialists. For many years they wrote reports about their young appearance and sexual potency. In 1927, about one thousand transplants had been performed by Voronoff himself or by his students all over the world. It was only possible to tell whether the graft had taken by examining it under a microscope. But who of the *newly born* could be expected to sacrifice himself for the sake of science? Just like Steinach, Voronoff was hardly taken seriously in the circles of official medicine, but this wonder doctor become a famous man to old bucks throughout the world.

The American professor Lespinasse managed to transplant testicular tissue - obtained from men shortly after death - into the stomach muscles of live, impotent men. If someone had committed suicide or there had been an execution, Lespinasse lost no time in going along and removing the testicles while they were as fresh as possible. In the meantime, the impotent recipient of the donor tissue was being made ready for the operation by his assistants. Unfortunately, the grafts were always rejected. (Until now, only a couple of men have had a successful testicle transplant. These were identical twins, of whom one had no testicles and the other had two. In China, non-donor-related testicular transplantations have been performed with very poor results in the long-term).

A young prison physician from San Quentin had it a little easier in 1918. His name was Leo Stanley. He transplanted the testicles of men who had been executed, into prisoners of varying ages. The men stayed in prison, however, and the study results remained dubious. After all, freedom is an extremely important aphrodisiac!

American doctors performed many other remarkable experiments. The book *The Male Hormone* by De Kruif, tells the history of professor Fred Koch and his student Clyde McGee, both from Chicago. Unconcernedly, they mashed, extracted, fractionated and distilled thousands of kilos of bulls' testicles - forever in the search of pure male sex hormone. From forty kilos of testicles they produced twenty milligrams of impure, but effective substance. A very unrealistic balance.

In 1929 it was time for human application. A twenty-six-year-old impotent man with sparse pubic hair, no growth of moustache or beard and with a high voice, received the substance for fifty-three days. And the result was that he ended up looking like a real man! He developed normal sexual desires with orgasmic feelings and ejaculation. Ultimate proof of the importance of the male sex hormone! However, disappointment had the upper hand. It would never be possible to obtain sufficient bulls' testicles for commercial use. Moreover, it cost a fortune to process the testicles.

The dynamic German chemist Adolf Butenlandt tried a different approach. He was working at Schering's chemical plant and collected thousands of litres of urine. The urine was obtained from policemen, in total about 25,000 litres - an olympic swimming pool full. He was convinced that it contained the active substance. Ultimately, he produced only a few crystals, which mainly consisted of androsterone, a degradation product of testosterone.

On 27 May 1935, the chemist Ernst Laqueur discovered the precise structural formula of the male sex hormone. He was head of an excellent research team at the Organon pharmaceutical company and he was also a professor of pharmacology in Amsterdam. He called the hormone testosterone; the title of his famous paper was *On crystalline male hormone from testicles*. He too had unfortunately required a great many kilos of bulls' testicles.

Then the miracle occurred that so many scientists had been waiting for: cholesterol could be changed into testosterone synthetically. This discovery was made by the Yugoslavian chemist Vladislav Ruzicka. He was employed by the Swiss company Ciba. Cod-liver oil and sheep fat, both rich in cholesterol, were the major raw materials. In 1939, Butenlandt and Ruzicka received the Nobel prize. Laqueur, like Koch, was completely passed by.

What are the present day views on testosterone? A real testosterone deficiency can occur as a result of certain diseases of the testicles, in men with the Klinefelter syndrome and in certain renal diseases. Nowadays experts agree that there is only an indication to administer testosterone in a very small percentage of men with impotence. If the testosterone level is normal, then it is not worthwhile to administer extra testosterone. This would only lead to unpleasant side-effects, such as liver disturbances, prostate enlargement or even prostate cancer.

The withering penis

The fact that long ago there were so many ways in which sperm cells could be deposited - some male animals tried to outstrip the others by developing methods to bring them as close as possible to the egg cell-led to the origination of the penis. The penis was to play an essential role in reproduction.

There are many different types of 'penis': the *aedeagus* of flies, mites and butterflies, the protuberances that some frogs have near the anus, the organ with which the ordinary honey bee copulates (which breaks off - and costs him his life - but also makes sure that no other drones can mate with the queen), the embolus of the gold spider, the anal fin of fish, the double-jointed penises of snakes, the proboscis of the dragonfly. These are all penises that are used to deposit male sperm cells within the female. Ostriches are particularly well-endowed. At the turn of the twentieth century, people made walking sticks from ostrich penises. Phalluses vary from small protuberances to the penis of a whale which, although it is usually safely tucked away in his body, can reach a length of 1.8 metres. In the icy, life-threatening freezing cold of the north pole, the ship's doctor of the Dutch explorer William Barentz's, doctor Melchior, tanned the only part of a whale's skin that could be tanned and made a waistcoat of it. Calvinistic as he was, he had his States Bible bound in the same material - penis leather. Penis, death and religion are very closely bonded.

Penis leather can also be made from the human penis. Anyone who does not believe this should visit the village of Wieuwerd in Friesland, a northern province of Holland. This village has a mysterious crypt in a small church built in 1200, which was discovered by coincidence in 1765. The bodies of the deceased who were laid to rest there centuries ago has never decomposed. One of the mummified bodies on show - that of goldsmith Stellingwerf - exhibits an almost intact penis, but it has totally turned to leather! In the charmingly illustrated folder about Wieuwerd, it says: 'After visiting the crypt you can enjoy a cup of coffee and a delicious slice of Dutch apple pie in the adjoining cafeteria'.

Penises of the deceased can literally lead their own lives. There are many tales about the late French emperor Napoleon. One of them is recounted in *De kleinzoon van de letterzetter* (1995) (*The Grandson of the Typesetter*) by the Flemish writer Pjeroo Roobjee. It is a historical fact that a post mortem was performed on the emperor in 1821. He appeared to have died of stomach cancer. That was fairly common in his family. The physician who conducted the post mortem stated that the imperial reproductive organs were small and inane, and clearly shrivelled and withered. 'To put history straight, it should be pointed out that before he died, the deceased must have been totally impotent'.

Roobjee tells how a priest who was present at the post mortem somehow managed to obtain Napoleon's penis and what happened to it then:

It suddenly turned up, after an odyssey of almost one and a half centuries that we know nothing about, and made its appearance at Christie's Fine Art Auctioneers in London in the nineteen fifties. According to a servant who attended the sale, the one inch long (2.54 cm) imperial penis showed great similarity with an extremely small seahorse.

The auctioneer spoke of a paltry, dried-up object. No one appeared to be interested in the penis, which was on offer for thirteen thousand guineas. Shortly afterwards, it was offered for sale in a mail-order catalogue. Once again, no one was interested:

In 1961, Napoleon's penis ultimately found a sound and worthy owner. That was an American urologist, who paid about three million eight hundred thousand dollars for the minuscule object. Alas, the owner of the gem was not to enjoy the sight of the Corsican seahorse for very long: last autumn, he was felled by thrombosis. Since then the penis has started a second odyssey and Napoleon's body is still resting in the crypt under the Dome des Invalides until the present day, without a penis.

The average length of a man's penis in erection is about three times that of an adult gorilla. The proportionately enormous penis of a man gives an indirect indication of the sex life of our predecessors. If we consider this in relation to evolution, then a relatively long penis might have been meant to frighten off other men.

This is certainly true in a few species of ape, but it probably does not work like that in humans. Or is a long penis meant to attract women? Or to increase sexual enjoyment? Neither possibility seem likely. Evolution biologists believe that in female animals that mate with more than one male, the male with the longest penis can deliver his sperm the most safely, in other words, he has the most chance of fathering offspring. The so-called sperm competition theory therefore offers an elegant explanation for the size of the penis.

Believe it or not, the vagina is a very dangerous place for a sperm cell - an acidic torture chamber. That is why a penis that reaches the back of the vagina has the advantage compared to one that cannot deliver its load so close to the egg cell. Fortunately, male semen contains the necessary alkali to neutralize the acid. The fact that it is an advantage to be able to deposit as many sperm cells as possible close to the egg cell, creates the notion in an evolution biological sense that the penis should grow longer. However, a penis that reaches further than the opening of the womb (the cervix) does not offer any extra advantage.

Koro

An extremely strange form of impotence occurs in China and south-east Asia. It is called *koro*. 'Koro' is originally a Malaysian word. It means the 'head of a tortoise'. It is a psychiatric disorder that chiefly affects elderly men. Such a patient is convinced that his penis will wither, retract into his abdomen (thus the word 'koro') and cause his death. Koro can be an expression of schizophrenia, severe depression, epilepsy, delirium, but it can also occur as a withdrawal symptom in association with heroin addiction. Very occasionally, koro is the result of a brain tumour.

Not unexpectedly, Dutch physicians working in the Dutch East Indies were the first to publish papers on this remarkable form of impotence in the scientific literature. Blonk was the very first. In 1895 he wrote:

Koro, under this name a disorder is known among the Buginese and Makasar tribes that as far as I know, has never been described before. According to sufferers of this disorder, they feel that at unexpected moments, their penis has the tendency to retract into their abdomen. In cases who do not receive immediate help, this will certainly happen and the patient will not survive. Sufferers are naturally extremely frightened. As soon as they notice the first symptoms, they take hold of their penis to prevent its retraction. Sometimes they are unable to maintain this position themselves and the therapy must be continued by another person. Hour after hour the penis must be held in this way, while in some cases this requires considerable force.

The Chinese call koro *suo-yang*. This means 'withering penis'. Many explanations have been given in answer to the question of why koro chiefly seems to occur in China. One of them is associated with Chinese philosophy and the yin-yang principle. This philosophy attributes two fundamental opposing forces to man, the world and the universe. 'Yang' is the symbol for, among other things, masculinity. 'Yin' is the symbol for, among other things, femininity. In men this means that an extreme loss of yang together with a surplus of yin can lead to problems. Nightly ejaculations and masturbation in this view lead to a loss of yang. Normal coitus, i.e. between husband and wife, results in a 'healthy' exchange between yin and yang fluids.

More than in any other culture, great use has been made and is still being made of remedies to stimulate potency. It is very understandable scientifically that there is a direct relationship between male potency and cosmic characteristics of the yang principle.

Koro also occurs in western cultures. In 1985, an article was published by Malinick and Flaherty in the *International Journal of Psychiatry* about a fifty-one year old American patient who in a state of extreme anxiety, and with palpitations of the heart and hyperventilation, reported to the casualty department. Just previously, he had visited a prostitute, who before performing oral sex, had washed his glans and penis in what the patient considered to be a strange chemical substance. Directly after this contact, his penis had started to wither. He had seen a strange sort of smile on her face and felt more or less 'bewitched'. He was frightened that he would soon die. He was admitted to hospital where it gradually became clear that he was schizophrenic and also drank too much alcohol.

In fifteenth century Europe, similar stories were recorded, but in this case by notorious witch-hunters instead of by psychiatrists. Which ever way you look at it, women nearly always get the blame!

Misunderstandings about the glans

Firstly, we must clear up a few misunderstandings about the glans penis. To start with, it is by no means the case that the penis is a very sensitive organ. In comparison with other parts of the body, the number of free nerve endings is extremely small. A relatively larger number of free nerve endings are only to be found on the under side of the glans. The second misunderstanding is that the penis has to go into action to obtain an erection. That is not true either. However, in order to stay flaccid, the smooth muscle cells in the cavernous bodies of the penis need to be contracted most of the time. During the night, in our deep dreams, and during sexual arousal, these smooth muscle cells can relax and the spongy network within the cavernous bodies becomes larger.

The third serious misunderstanding is that the glans (according to Dickinson in 1933) has become soft and pliable in the course of evolution so that it will not cause too much damage to the woman during coitus. This interpretation is incorrect. The glans forms the outer end of the spongy body, i.e. the erectile body that surrounds the urethra. Just as in the pair of cavernous erectile bodies (the corpora cavernosa) the pressure increases in the spongy body during erection, but not as much as in the corpora cavernosa. Otherwise the urethra would be pinched closed and the semen would not be able to reach its intended destination.

Relatively little attention has been paid to the glans by poets. Only the French poet Paul Verlaine wrote an ode to the glans in his poem 'Hombres': 'my dainty morsel, with its emission of godly phosphorus'. The poem forms part of a collection that was published after his death, clandestinely. With the words the poet put himself on stage, licking and revelling, in his enjoyment of the love of women, but also hankering for the love of men.

In ancient Greece, participants in the Olympic games were naked. However, only the glans was not allowed to be shown, because that was considered vulgar. For this reason, a ribbon was wrapped around the foreskin.

Certain animal species also have 'decorations' on their penis. In ruminants, the spherical glans tapers off into a threadlike appendage that reaches into the uterus during copulation. In the ram, for example, the appendage is four centimetres long. In carnivores and insectivores, the glans has spikes and thorns. At rest, these lie hidden in a sort of pouch, whereas in erection they stick out and promote extra vaginal stimulation in the female.

Humans do not have such protuberances. However, in the scientific literature almost one hundred patients have been described with some type of abnormality. In the majority of cases this comprises a sort of horn; in thirty per cent of them cancer is to blame. Fortunately, treatment is simple and usually adequate: the affected part is removed surgically. Urologists call this partial penis amputation.

In certain cultures, the men furnish their glans with protuberances. In the nineteenth century, this was common practice among the Javanese. They made incisions in several places and subsequently inserted small stones into the openings. After the wounds had healed, the glans had an irregular, bumpy surface, which was intended to provide extra stimulation for the vagina.

With the same intention, the Dayaks and other primitive peoples bored a hole from left to right through the glans and pushed a bamboo pipe or bone through the hole. During daily activities, the bone was replaced by a feather; the bone was only worn on feast days. Only the chief of the tribe had the right to introduce a second hole.

In Europe, too, many people have been seeking ways to increase a woman's pleasure during coitus. In the eighteenth century, Frenchmen used penis rings with hard protuberances. These were called *aides*. In Russia, men used rings that were fitted with little white teeth. In South

America, they used horse hair. The present-day condom with ridges is the newest variation.

The genital organs of the kamikaze honey bee drone are also adorned with yellowish protuberances and all sorts of frills and whiskers. These appendages burst during orgasm inside the queen bee and in this way form a natural chastity belt which closes the entrance against other suitors, even when the drone falls to the ground and dies.

Some rodents and feline species are endowed with the presence of actual foreskin glands. Consider beaver gel, musk or civet (feline species). Quite a large group of women use these every day. If one assumes that perfumes are meant to attract men, then it is remarkable that women use the glandular secretions of male animals. After all, men loathe these male scents.

Homo sapiens also have foreskin glands, but these are often a source of much concern and misery. A great many patients think that they have caught a venereal disease when they first discover the sebaceous glands on the underside of their glans.

In another category of patients who are not used to pulling back the foreskin each day and washing underneath, sebaceous excretions accumulate under the foreskin. Doctors call this smegma. It is a whitish substance, with the consistency of bath soap, which accumulates in the folds of the genital organs. According to some scientists, smegma can cause cancer. Urology nurses have plenty of work with the penis every day and, in somewhat elderly gentlemen, with smegma. This is because before the urologist can look inside the bladder, the penis has to be disinfected to prevent infection. These nurses witness a great deal in this respect. For instance, one of our theatre nurses from the province of Groningen speaks in terms of 'farmers who make their own cheese'. After all, disinfecting a minimum of fifteen penises per day is certainly not a sinecure. One nurse might say to the patient: 'I'll just give it a bit of a polish', another might say: 'I'll just give it a bit of a wash, while a stray male nurse might say: 'I'll just clean him for you'. The latter sounds the most natural, and also the most friendly.

Tumescence and detumescence

It is only in very few men that the penis stands completely vertical, namely in about ten per cent. In about fifteen to twenty per cent, the erection angle is about 45 degrees above horizontal. In nearly all cases, the angle is above the horizontal plane.

Many young men worry about what they consider to be a crookedly-hanging penis. They blame this on too much masturbation. Their worry is totally unfounded. Every man's penis is crooked to some extent. In the past, all tailors knew this and adjusted the cut of the trousers accordingly: 'Do you dress on the left or the right, sir?' was the usual question. On the basis of interviews conducted in the nineteen fifties, the American researcher Kinsey claimed that about seventy to eighty per cent of the men dressed on the left. This was confirmed through scientific research by radiologists. They investigated the position of the penis - whether it was hanging on the left or right - on a large series of X-rays of the lower abdomen. On a plain X-ray (i.e. without contrast medium) the penis is easily visible as a 'soft tissue shadow', as it is called in doctor's jargon.

In radiodiagnostics, sexology is gaining more and more interest. In 1994, magnetic resonance imaging (MRI) was used to obtain images of the internal anatomy during coitus. MRI is a method which can produce very informative images of the whole human body and in all planes and directions. During this MRI examination a (married) couple had sex 'on command' in the narrow tunnel of the MR equipment. The results showed that the penis penetrates a woman's body much further than physicians had assumed until then. This explains why some women experience pain during coitus.

The penis is a large blood sausage that comprises three compartments or spongy erectile bodies. If during sexual stimulation a lot of blood flows in and very little flows out, then the penis will become hard and stiff. An erection occurs. The pair of erectile bodies in the upper part of the penis - the *corpora cavernosa* - are filled first and afterwards the third erectile body, the corpus spongiosum. The two upper erectile bodies are joined together at various places. The inner ends are attached to the pubic bone. On the upper side there is a sort of lever between these two erectile bodies and the upper part of the pubic bone. This is to prevent the penis from wobbling in erection. The third erectile body surrounds the urethra and ends in the glans penis. The glans is covered by the foreskin, which must be able to be drawn back freely. Beneath the skin of the penis, there is a thin layer of connective tissue plus a much thicker sheet. This fibrous sheet encloses the erectile bodies (the tunica albuginea).

Owing to the fact that an erection occurs due to the congestion of blood in the erectile bodies, it is important that the supplying arteries are intact. These comprise the abdominal aorta, which splits into two arteries at the level of the pelvis. Branches from these arteries also go to the legs, buttocks and penis. The latter branches (one on the left and one on the right) are called the pudendal arteries. These two pudendal arteries split into a further three branches each: one goes to the upper side of the penis, one through each corpus cavernosum and one through the corpus spongiosum. The arteries that supply the corpora cavernosa are the most important ones: at that site innumerable branches are given off and these form connections with the veins that drain the organ. These veins develop into the larger veins in the erectile bodies, which in turn drain into the vena cava in the abdomen.

In order to produce an erection, the arteries must dilate, the muscles in the spongy tissue of the erectile bodies must relax and the draining veins must be somewhat compressed. This occurs under the influence of nerve stimulation. In the spinal cord, there are two *erection centres*, one at the level of the sacrum and one at the level of the lumbar spine. If, for example, a spinal fracture has paralysed the lower half of the body, manual manipulation of the penis can result in an erection, so-called reflex erection. As soon as the stimulation stops, the erection is lost. Coitus is therefore impossible and the same applies to achieving a 'normal' orgasm. Some patients with a spinal cord lesion say that they can reach a sort of climax, but that the pleasurable sensations are not localised in the lower abdomen, but at the level of the zone where the loss of feeling starts.

If the penis is a blood sausage, is it also edible? Yes. The recipe originates from a very poor Jewish-Yemenite kitchen: Blanch the ram/ goat penis and clean it thoroughly. Boil for ten minutes and then slice thinly. Fry onions, garlic and coriander in a little oil. Add the penis and continue frying. Mix together chopped tomato, pepper, cumin, saffron and salt and pour over the penis. Cover the pan and simmer gently for two hours.

In Holland, you are not likely to be able to acquire a penis easily. According to the meat inspection laws, any penises that become available through slaughter must be destroyed. 'Genital organs may not be made into or used to produce meat products and may not be present at locations meant for the preparation or conservation of meat.' These prohibitions probably originate from the fact that Brucellosis was a common disease at the beginning of the century. This infection is chiefly located in the testis and epididymis and perhaps also in the urethra of slaughtered animals. Humans might become infected if they eat these parts. The pizzles used to flog squatters, for instance, come from abroad.

The dentate vagina

Some men are unable to surrender themselves. They are cowards full of macho bluff! Their penis goes flaccid the moment they try to manoeuvre it into the vagina. This is not real impotence. The cause is deeply rooted anxiety of loosing their beloved organ. Fear of the *dentate vagina*, the vagina with sharp teeth that can bite off a man's penis. The dentate vagina plays an important role in an African legend: beautiful girls descended to the earth from the heavens and they repeatedly stole the hunters catch. When a man who was on watch caught one of the girls, he shot her. His attempt to rape her cost him his genital organ: her vagina was equipped with extremely sharp teeth with which she bit off his penis.

The dentate vagina is also mentioned in a centuries old Siberian legend. This story ends reasonably favourably for the man. On one of his forays, the hunter met a one-eyed cave dweller. She claimed him as her husband. He hesitated. Her large breasts were to his liking, but her strange face put him off. In addition, from somewhere within her body he could hear what sounded like grinding teeth. After she had fallen asleep, he investigated where the sound was coming from. Between her legs he discovered two rows of teeth. The hunter then thought up a trick. He looked for an oblong stone. When the woman woke up and demanded sex from him, he stuck the stone between her legs and the secret teeth ground themselves to dust on the hard material and her vagina became the same as that of all other women. Ultimately, the man took the woman home as his slave.

The modern feministic literature also mentions the dentate vagina. In 1993 *The Second Coming* was published in the Netherlands under the title *Het Orgasme*. This was the first novel by the Greek writer Euridice Kamvisseli. Ela, the heroin in the novel, is the proud owner of a marvellous tight and greedy genital organ, which is described in many different ways. She has a fanclub of hundreds of exlovers who wear a coloured ribbon around their penis which reflects their position in the strict hierarchy of sexual performance. In the book there are frightening passages, including the one below from the prologue:

> *That is why Ela offers her cunt freely to men, as if she is the eloquent head of John the Baptist, presented neatly on a tray. She gives them permission to try their luck with her and not to spare her. 'Do not confuse my cunt with glory' Ela warns the men, hoping to swing the balance, 'enter at your own risk'. Then they burst out in arrogant laughter. Not long afterwards, her cunt devours every scrap of them...*

How often should a man ejaculate

According to old Asian wisdom, 'When, in the first year that they know each other, a couple always puts a bean into a pot when they have sex, then it will take a whole married-lifetime for them to empty the pot if they remove a bean from the pot each time they have sex after that year'. The question of how often sexual intercourse should take place has not only been occupying us, but also the founders of religion, philosophy and legislation. The prophet Mohammed, who, unlike many other founders of religion, had great respect for women, recommended *once a week* in the Koran. That is also a woman's right, irrespective of the number of wives a man has.

The Jewish Talmud is less general. Distinctions are made between different types of people. For a strong and healthy young man, who is not forced to work hard, once a day is advised. For the ordinary workman, twice a week and for men of learning once a week. Professors could receive dispensation. They were only required to have sexual relations once every two years. Martin Luther considered twice a week to be the correct measure. The Pope advised coitus only if the couple wanted to have children.

Legislators are indirectly occupied with the frequency of coitus. Within a marriage in Holland, neither the wife nor the husband can be forced to have sex. Marital rape is punishable by law. In other words, the legislator considers that no sex is also OK! A recent Dutch study has shown that 96 per cent of couples have sexual intercourse one or more times per two months.

Kinsey stated that a man's age is the deciding factor for his sex life. He was a real number freak. The following figures are derived from his statistics about the average coitus frequency per week:

between 26 and 30   2.24
between 31 and 40   1.73
between 41 and 45   1.41
between 46 and 50   1.10
between 51 and 55   0.90
between 56 and 60   0.73
between 61 and 65   0.52
between 66 and 70   0.30
between 71 and 75   0.00

Kinsey's figures correspond nicely, don't they? Every reader will glance at his own age category or that of her partner. Impotent men might be assisted by the following American rule of thumb about coitus frequency in relation with age:

younger than 25:	*twice daily*
25-35:	*tri-weekly*
35-45:	*try-weekly*
45-55:	*try-weakly*
older than 55:	*try, try, try*

The way to explain how ejaculation works, is to compare it with rifle-shooting. First you have to load. The urethra has the function of the barrel of the rifle. Ejaculation changes as a man gets older. Both the emission and expulsion phases take longer. 'Emission' is the same as loading, while 'expulsion' is the same as firing. In the emission phase, a mixture of sperm cells, seminal and prostate fluid are forced into the urethra by strong contractions of the epididymis, seminal vesicles, seminal ducts and the prostate. In the 'expulsion phase', the prostate and the muscles under the urethra contract periodically and eject the semen from the penis at 0.8 second intervals. Adolescents sometimes like to boast about how far they can 'shoot'. In a certain tribe in New Guinea, they even do this as a party game. The length of the shot of ejaculation has never been studied scientifically.

The quantity of semen ejaculated each time by a man is about two to four millilitres after 24 to 36 hours of sexual abstinence. A modest quantity in comparison with that produced by a male pig (boar). He ejaculates half a litre each time, so I was told by a veterinary-urology surgeon. First year women medical students are usually surprised when they hear this during the sexology lectures. According to the American urologist Metcalf, the world record in men is half a tea cup full. Incidentally, during the making of porno-films, the male actor who has to ejaculate is required to abstain for several days, so that the portion is as large as possible. If you ask a man how many millilitres he ejaculates, he will probably guess too high. This also applied to the members of a pop group in the nineteen seventies. They called themselves *Ten CC*, oh yes, all on account of the estimated quantity. Two of their songs were 'I'm not in love' and 'The things we do for love'. In the nineteen sixties, there was a pop group called 'Lovin Spoonful', which was also related with the ejaculation volume.

The greatest portion of the semen is produced by both testicles, the prostate gland and to a lesser extent by Cowper's glands. The seminal ducts lie on either side at the back of the prostate. They discharge directly into the seminal vesicles, just before they enter the prostate. They produce almost eighty per cent of the seminal fluid. The fluid is clear and contains fructose (fruit sugar). It is a bit syrupy owing to the sugar. The seminal vesicles subsequently enter the prostate. They run through the prostate and emerge in the urethra. The prostate produces about twenty per cent of the seminal volume and causes the milky-white appearance. Sometimes it might be yellowish. Further downstream and towards the front, are Cowper's glands. They also discharge into the urethra and produce the crystal-clear fluid that is often excreted before the actual ejaculation. It is not surprising that in sex education books, this is called fore fluid.

During ejaculation, the neck of the bladder is tightly closed to prevent the semen from entering the bladder. After a prostate operation, the semen nearly always enters the bladder, because the neck of the bladder can no longer be closed. The closure mechanism is irreparably damaged by the operation. The semen is discharged the next time the man urinates.

After ejaculation, the semen immediately coagulates. It looks somewhat congealed, like egg white that has been heated. About a quarter of an hour later, this jelly runs and turns back into a liquid.

Premature ejaculation

Very premature ejaculation is by far the most common sexual inadequacy in men. 'Premature' in this sense means ejaculation almost directly after the penis has entered the vagina - a sort of masturbation in the vagina - or even before the penis has entered the vagina, or in other words 'ante portam' as some doctors describe it.

In animals, this is better organised. In the dog for example, further swelling of the penis occurs after the penis has entered the bitch's vagina. Consequently, after the dog has ejaculated in a relatively narrow vagina - ponder the situation of an alsatian dog with a poodle bitch - he will not be able to withdraw his penis for some time. This can take from a couple of minutes to an hour or so. Postponed withdrawal not only prevents semen from being spilt and wasted, but also means that the animals are permitted a feeling of intimacy and unity at a very tender moment. Owners often try to cut this moment short with buckets of cold water, but that does not help at all.

In his anthology *Een gondel in de Herengracht* (1978) (*A Gondola in the Heren Canal*) A.F.Th. van der Heijden describes a variation of the dentate vagina.

The father of the central figure tells that as a results of war trauma, he still has a bullet in his head. As a result, he becomes unconscious if he exerts himself to much. After being admitted to hospital, he falls in love with one of the nurses, and she with him. On her day off, they quietly slip away together. She turns out to be the persistent type. His report on the first and also the last time that they make love:

> ...*after I collapsed on top of her, just at the point of ejaculation. In reaction, or rather from fear that I was dead, at the same moment she had an acute vaginal cramp, which meant that she could not loosen herself from me. (...) Recovering from the first shock (I was still alive) she had to wait until I was soft enough to worm my way out of her. But her cramp would not stop. For hours she lay beneath me, concentrating on her belly. But the more she tried to relax her muscles, the worse the cramp became. In this way she strangled me tighter and tighter within herself. She lay like that for hours.*

Evolution biologists often have very refreshing ideas about sexuality. They believe that in the course of evolution, male mammals have actually taught themselves to reach orgasm and ejaculate as quickly as possible. If you are small and sitting on top of a female, you form an easy prey for passing enemies. The rat for example, climbs on, penetrates and ejaculates within a few seconds. Larger animals can permit themselves to take things a little more as their ease. A lion is perfectly aware of course that he does not have to keep looking over his shoulder. He can take his time, just like the rhinoceros.

The Swedish landbug also likes long coitus; he usually takes about twenty-four hours. The male not only has a long penis that is about two thirds of the length of his body, but his penis is also equipped with hooks so that it cannot pop out easily after he has entered the female. Owing to the fact that the penis can be kept so solidly in place, the partners have a long union. This type of excessive protuberance probably evolved in order to keep unwilling females under control.

Premature ejaculation never has a physical cause. From a psychoanalytical point of view it has been suggested that premature ejaculation originates from unconscious dormant sadistic feelings towards women. Modern sexological research has not been able to confirm this theory. The problem may have something to do with unpleasant sexual experience at a young age, such as coitus interruptus, having to make love on the back seat of a car, fear of being discovered, or a first sexual encounter with a prostitute who was only interested in quick ejaculation.

Coitus is the most intimate thing that two people can do together. It is in fact a very risky situation, letting another person get so close to you. It could make you very nervous, especially when you realise that at a certain moment you will lose control of yourself, namely at the moment of orgasm.

The first scientific description of coitus in the Dutch literature was published in 1916 by the urologist Van der Vuurst de Vries:

As soon as the male member enters the vestibule (entrance to the vagina) the glans penis first rubs against the glans clitoris that lies at the beginning of the genital canal, which through its position and angle, can turn aside and bend. After the first stimulation of both these sensitive centres, the glans penis slides over the two bulbar ridges, so that the body of the penis is enclosed within them, while the glans penis continually rubs the fine and fragile surface of the vaginal mucous lining. The latter is elastic, owing to the erectile tissue situated between the separate layers and is therefore capable of closing tightly around the penis. The blood is pushed out of the vessels in the vaginal wall towards both bulbar ridges and the clitoris, which makes them more erect and increases the sensitivity of the clitoris. In addition, the clitoris is pulled downwards by muscular activity, against the glans penis. In this way they rub against each other, such that by each movement of copulation, both sexes are stimulated more and more and ultimately with increasing sensuality, a level of orgasm is reached that on the male side leads to ejaculation and on the female side opens the uterine cervix and enables the semen to enter.

This uro-sexologist, who ahead of his time, had made it clear that the man *and* the woman can enjoy sex, follows his exposé with a description of general phenomena during coitus:

While in one of the partners the pleasurable feelings are revealed by hardly noticeable trembling, the other experiences the greatest mental and physical arousal. Between the two, there are innumerable transitions. Accelerations in blood circulation, strongly beating arteries; venous blood is retained in the veins by muscle contractions and increases the feeling of warmth. This venous blood retention, which occurs more strongly in the brain through contraction of the neck muscles and bending backwards of the neck, causes temporary congestion in the brain and extinguishes all mental functions. The eyes, that have become red through injection of the retina, stare and take on an uncertain look, or as usually happens, they close firmly so as not to be stung by the light.
*   The breathing, that in one partner is short and halting, is broken*

in the other through strong contractions of the larynx, and the temporarily compressed air is forcibly expelled with incoherent and unintelligible sounds.

Movements, as well as feelings, display an undescribable confusion in expression. The limbs jerk or even cramp up and flail in all directions or stretch until they are as rigid as sticks; tightly clenched jaws cause grinding teeth; some people in their 'erotic delirium' even go so far that without regard for the other person, they bite and draw blood from a carelessly bared shoulder. This nervous state, this epilepsy, is usually short-lived, but long enough to totally exhaust the organism, especially the man, who follows this overstraining with a more or less lavish ejaculation. Then comes an exhausted state, whose importance coincides with the preceding arousal intensity. This sudden exhaustion, this general weakness and tendency towards sleep, that hits the man after coitus, can partly be attributed to sperm loss, while the woman, however powerfully she might have participated in the proceedings, only feels a short period of listlessness, which is much weaker that the man's and enables her to have further coitus much earlier and more frequently. Galenus has already said: 'Triste est omne animal post coitum, praeter mulierum gallumque' (Every animal is in a sombre mood after coitus, except for the woman and the cockrel). [That is really taking the man under protection!]

In the majority of mammals, coitus involves the male approaching the female from behind. Only whales form an exception to this and sometimes the primates by way of variation. Most animals always mate in the same way. No matter how peculiarly tender or, to the other extreme, brutal, nothing changes. The cock-pigeon courts and circles around the hen. The praying mantis eats her mate after mating. These rituals have always been the same. A daunting and marvellous monotony that in humans becomes, or to put it a better way, can become a daunting and marvellous variety. In humans, the woman can also be approached from behind. In some peoples this is even the rule.

For instance, it is said of the inhabitants of Madagascar that coitus usually takes place in this manner. For a change they use the vis-à-vis position. They call this the 'missionary position'. Europeans turn to face each other and the position is determined ethnographically. In Western Europe, the preference is the back and the woman underneath, whereas in the Mediterranean region, 'the woman rides the man' as Homer put it. But we have digressed.

Let us return to premature ejaculation. The greatest objection is that the partner does not reach orgasm. The man may be able to compromise with a second coitus. Some men can manage that within half an hour, but generally several hours are needed. The majority of men will only be able to have several orgasms one after the other before puberty. A single orgasm with a so-called refraction period is the price that a man must pay for ejaculation. In contrast, women can have multiple orgasms. The vast majority of men have the tendency to withdraw from the vagina after ejaculation. Any further rubbing is experienced as unpleasant. The work is finished and for the moment, there is not really anything more to do.

Nowadays, it is believed that premature ejaculation originates from a disrupted conditioning process. This means that sex therapy (talking and practising) often helps. But as is also the case with impotence, many men want to be treated with pills. In America, Prozac and Anafranil are popular drugs in this respect. What might also help as an antidote when approaching the supreme moment, is thinking about something else, for example a herd of trudging elephants or vomit.

In urological practice, the doctor often encounters strange patients in this respect. For example, I was consulted by a couple who had been married for six years. They asked whether I had any effective means of preventing premature ejaculation. The patient mentioned that he had started to suffer from premature ejaculation shortly after his wife had become pregnant. He was afraid of damaging the fetus. Up to this point, everything was very understandable, because this unspoken anxiety probably occurs in many expectant fathers.

Nevertheless, the problem had never disappeared. Every time, after three coitus movements, the husband ejaculated. His wife had something more to add - she could only reach orgasm through vaginal stimulation.

The couple agreed to try using a sort of anaesthetic jelly. About twenty minutes before the planned coitus, the man had to rub it into his glans.

While they were standing in the doorway, the wife decided to ask another question. She asked whether it would do any harm to put her husband's penis in her mouth, because she always did that first.

'No', I said without moving a muscle.

Something more should be said about this anaesthetic jelly or creme. It can be obtained at almost any chemist and will partially anaesthetize the penis. It becomes less sensitive, which might help prevent premature ejaculation. The jelly does not always work and it impairs part of the pleasure. If the man does not use a condom, the mucous membrane of the vagina (and of the mouth) will also lose sensitivity.

Italian urologists have thought of a rigorous solution. They simply cut through the branches of the dorsal pudic nerve. According to the first Italian report from Sienna, at least half of the patients were able to postpone ejaculation for five minutes six months after the procedure.

Aging also improves the situation of premature ejaculation. A nice example can be found in the French literature in Francoise Sagan's novel *Un Certain Sourire* (*A Far Away Smile*). The novel is pervaded by a rare tiredness, by satedness and boredom that does not befit the youthfulness of the leading lady. With icy indifference she starts a relationship with Luc, the uncle of her boyfriend Bertrand. She makes a comparison between her young lover Bertrand and her older lover Luc. Her preference is clearly for Luc. He not only kisses better, but also understands the art of postponing ejaculation. With him love-play is not choked by eagerness.

The length of the penis

'My boyfriend has a tiny poke/ But otherwise he's a real good bloke'.

Few poets have written openly about the penis. For a discussion about the length, the literature offers very little. Hendrik Overganck has written various poems about the penis in his anthology *De Tooverstaf* (The magic wand).

At a young age, sometimes under concealment, the complaint is put forward that: he is not well-blessed. According to the American sexologist Barry McCarthy, two out of three men think that their penis is too small. He attributes the worries they have about the length of their penis to various factors. To start with, little boys see their father's penis for the first time at a 'sensitive' age. Secondly, in a changing room, men usually see other men from the front. Apparently, the other man's penis is larger because a man can only see his own penis from above. From above, you have an effect that artists refer to as 'shortening'. The penis looks smaller than it really is. Thirdly, there are considerable differences in the lengths of flaccid penises, while in erection there is not much difference. Fourthly, men generally do not know all that much about the subject, because they do not like to talk openly about such intimate matters.

The problem of a small penis is many centuries old. In the eighteenth century, it was usual practice for midwives in Normandy to cut the umbilical cord of new born boys as far away from the abdomen as possible. If it was bandaged too tightly before it was cut and then cut off too short, it would pull the penis inside.

In 1899, the German physician Loeb performed a study on fifty men aged between 18 and 35 years. The length of the visible part of the flaccid penis varied from 8 to 11 centimetres (average 9.4 cm) and the circumference from 8 to 10.5 cm.

The Kinsey report showed that only one quarter of men had a average-size penis. However, extremes were fairly rare. Five per cent of the men had an erection of less that 9 cm and one per cent were very well-endowed with an erection of longer than 20 cm.

Doctor Jacobus X was the pseudonym of the surgeon in the French army who spent many years of his life examining and measuring hundreds of male and female genital organs from all corners of the world. A comparative study - that was his field of interest. In 1935 he published his results. African men had the longest penises: flaccid 12.5 to 15 cm, in erection 19 to 20 cm. Jacobus also observed that the size of the penis was always closely linked with the size of the vagina of each particular race. 'Hindu women whose men have a short and thin penis, will have trouble with the average European', wrote the army doctor. 'The enormous penis of the African man would, in their view, be an instrument of torture'.

Jacobs seems to be saying that mother nature has made sure that members of the same race seek each other out. The mixing of races would be unnatural. Nowadays this notion is frowned upon, but in the nineteen thirties such ideas were not uncommon.

In the past, doctors associated the size of the nose with the size of the genital organs. Later that turned out to be nonsense. However, there is a so-called *nosogenital alliance*; the late Dutch professor Vroon has written about it. In his opinion, there are complicated forms of cooperation between the sense of smell, sex hormones and the sex drive. Apart from this, there is a sort of anatomical relationship between the erectile bodies in the penis or clitoris and the mucous lining of the nose that has a tendency to swell up to some extent. Consequently, sexually aroused people have a little difficulty breathing through their nose. Sometimes a man has to sneeze when he is confronted by an attractive woman. In ancient Rome, if a man committed adultery, his nose was cut off instead of his penis.

In Piesol's textbook of anatomy from 1907, it says that in comparison with other organs, the size of the penis is not related to the level of general physical development. You cannot judge the length of a man's penis by looking at his nose, contrary to what some mother-in-law's maintain. According to the scholars Siminoski and Bain, there **is** a statistically significant relationship between shoe size and the length of the penis.

A special form of small penis, is the webbed penis. It is not small in fact, but is seems so because the penis and the skin of the scrotum are joined together with a sort of webbing. Usually it is sufficient to incise the skin in a transverse direction and stitch the wounds longitudinally.

Every so often, politicians also have involvement with an erect penis. In 1993 a discussion arose in European Parliament about the length of the penis. Mrs Nel van Dijk, parliamentary member of *Groen-Links* (Green-Left party) recommended ending 'the squabbling about EC norms for the condom'. What was the problem? For just about anything you can think of, there have to be EC norms. The English were fighting for a compromise about the length of the average European penis. According to them, an average length of 17 cm and a diameter of 5.6 cm was far too small. The average English penis is believed to be quite a bit bigger.

Nel van Dijk asked the committee whether they were of the opinion that in view of the sensitivity obviously surrounding establishing the average length of the penis, it might be wise to let each country decide their own average length, or at least to discuss the matter on a lower level than the European Committee. Another possibility was making a charter for the condom. The member countries could if necessary ask for exceptions to be made about the statistically estimated average length.

'And if the gentlemen get stuck, then the male member itself will no doubt need to be *normalised*. I wonder what measures the busybodies in Brussels will come up with for accomplishing that.' What wisdom in these words!

Under the authority of the Amsterdam condom manufacturer *Het Gulden Vlies* (*The Golden Fleece*), the psychologist Erick Janssen performed a study on the circumference of the penis in erection. If a condom is too tight, this can lead to complaints, ranging from 'doesn't feel comfortable' to 'it is strangling me'. In contrast, a condom that is too loose, can slip off by accident. Janssen's study showed that measured around the base, the average circumference of the penis in full erection was about 121 millimetres, with a range from 90 to 161 mm. Thus, the range was very wide. In addition, in a quarter of the study subjects, the circumference of the penis in erection was less than

110 mm, in three quarters less that 130 mm and in ninety per cent less than 140 mm. In ten per cent, the circumference in erection was more than 140 mm.

The researcher's conclusion was that good instruction about condoms should always contain information about the thickness of the penis in relation to various sizes of condom.

In ancient Tantric texts, the length of the penis was measured from the perineum (i.e. starting from under the testicles). In this way, penis lengths of 25 to 30 cm were quite normal. Perhaps we western Europeans are underestimating ourselves. Maybe it would feel 'fuller and more whole' if the testicles are included in the measurements.

In 1967, the American scholar Havelock Elliott published his study *On Penises*, in which there is a mine of information about the size of the penis and especially about the correlation between the size and other characteristics. He found that participants in athletics not only had a longer penis on average, but also a significantly thicker one. In swimmers, in contrast, the penis was on the small side in more than eighty per cent.

Elliott also studied the relationship between penis length and political preferences. The American republicans scored noticeably higher than the democrats, while the most conservative republicans within the party were the most well-endowed of all. The hypothesis that men with left-wing sympathies are likely to be undersized, appeared to be true in 69.8% of the cases. The suggestion that a man might be able to alter the length of his penis by voting for a different party, was dismissed by this researcher.

Increasing the length of the penis

Throughout the centuries, men have been trying to make their penis longer. The most primitive way is to hang stones on it. That works, but also causes impotence. In addition, there is the Polynesian stretching method using a moveable heavy pipe, the Arabian 'Jelq' treatment (massage) and the 'Penicure' method based on the latter technique. In the USA, you can buy equipment that performs massages according to the Jelq method. The manufacturer claims that within twenty weeks, you can achieve an increase of two and a half centimetres in length. You can read all about it in *Penis enlargement methods* by the American Gary Griffin.

According to Jolan Chang, writer of the book *The Tao of Love and Sex*, the answer lies particularly in practising. Taoists believe that every part of the body can be trained and developed. It was the Chinese, of course, who invented physiotherapy! The Tao method does not use any artificial means or aids. Chang described it affectionately:

If, in communion, a man's jade stem is long and large enough to fit his partner's vulva completely, he usually can please her with less effort. It is often said that if one wishes to do a good job he must first sharpen his tool. One should know that there is a way to enlarge a deficient phallus. Every morning, any time after the hour of tzu [midnight] to before the hour of wu [noon], the time when the power of Yin is diminishing and that of Yang dominating, he should sit in a quiet room facing east meditating. He should concentrate his spirit and cut off his worries. His stomach should neither be too full nor too empty. He should expire impure air from his lungs and inhale to fill them with fresh air deep down to his abdomen. He should thus breathe deep forty-nine times. Then he should rub his palms together until they are hot as fire. Next he uses his right hand holding his scrotum and his yu heng, his left hand rubs his abdomen beneath the navel in the round and round manner turning left for eighty-one times and then he uses his right hand rubbing the same spot in the same manner except turning right for another eighty-one times. Then he stretches his right hand and lifts his yu heng from its root swinging and shaking it left and right hitting both legs numerous times. Then he hugs his woman and gently thrusts his yu heng into her house of Yin [vulva], nurtures it with his woman's secretions and breathes in his woman's breath [in the ancient view woman's breath could be nourishing to the male and vice versa].

After this he should use his palms rubbing his jade peak in the manner of making a thread from fibres uncountable times. If he does this long enough he will in time notice it growing bigger and longer. [Wu does not say for how long each day nor how many days to continue this exercise. Presumably until the man has noticed that there is some effect.

Urologists can also do something about a penis that is too small. Paediatric urologists for instance, sometimes prescribe a short course of testosterone for young boys, with the aim of temporarily enlarging the penis. The mothers are asked to rub testosterone creme into their son's penis on a daily basis. In this way, surgical correction of congenital abnormalities is easier to perform. In adults, the situation is more difficult, to the disappointment of many. Testosterone cremes or ointments have far less effect. Some men do benefit though, particularly those who have a 'dead feeling' in their groin. However, there is one rather unfortunate side-effect: the anointed penis should not be introduced into the vagina, because the ointment or creme will be absorbed easily and rapidly through the vaginal wall. Although this will lead to an increase in her libido, the woman might also grow a mustache. And that certainly is not the idea!

In the Netherlands, there is even a club for adult men who think that their penis is too small, called *De Pinkeltjes* (The Pinkies). The club was founded in 1990. According to the club news in the *Gaykrant* of 13 May 1995, they had twenty members at that time. Despite considerable publicity, this lustrum was celebrated in austerity. There is also an international group, under the name *Small Etc.*. In the homo-world there is also a club for very well-endowed men, called *The Horsemen*. Only five per cent of the members are heterosexual.

In the summer of 1993, the members of *De Pinkeltjes* were pleasantly surprised to read in the *Gaykrant* that in South Africa, more than one hundred *penis lengthening operations* had been performed. When asked, the plastic surgeon from Johannesburg commented: 'A month after the operation, the patients could resume their normal sex life. It leaves a scar that goes down as far as the scrotum. The patient with a relatively large penis can become impotent. Reasons included anxiety about hurting their partner during coitus and the fact that they had been rejected at some stage owing to the large size of their penis.

A physician called Smit described the problems involved with a too large or a too small penis in 1810:

The immoderateness caused by the largeness or smallness of the male member, is extremely relative. The case that a too well-endowed man is unsuitable to complete his marital duties, is very rare. Young women feel some amount of pain, because of the over-solidity of the member, but this soon turns into the most pleasant of sensations. The female vagina is distinguished with regard to its width and depth. Women of experience have less of a problem with excessive thickness, than with excessive length. The vagina is normally six or eight inches deep. If the male member exceeds this length, then it will aggravate the internal mouth of the womb. Women whose uterine mouth is sore, experience the most discomfort from a too substantial member and the heavy thrusts against the very sensitive uterine mouth have often led to dangerous fits, inflammation and even bruising. The use of the well-known rings to prevent disasters, is most applicable in these circumstances. If the member, however long it might be, is also thin and pointed, then it might penetrate the womb easily and after some time, be admitted with willingness.

2
Impotence

Surprisingly little is known about the number of men who have erectile problems. Probably, every man will have problems at some time during his life. Usually, these problems disappear by themselves. However, it is not clear how many men have persistent problems. There are no hard figures, because it is not a problem that men make a show of.

Primary impotence, i.e. impotence that originates in youth, is very rare. It is estimated that one in seven hundred men suffer from it. Secondary impotence is much more common. In an American study on one hundred men with an average age of 36 years, 7% had problems getting an erection and 9% mentioned problems with maintaining an erection. It was not clear how often they suffered from these problems or whether they were troubled by them. The exact prevalence of impotence is difficult to estimate because this condition is not life-threatening and men being treated represent only a small portion of the affected population. In a small survey of 109 men in the United Kingdom who were 16 to over 65 years of age, 32% reported some difficulty in achieving an erection during sexual stimulation and 20% had some difficulty in maintaining an erection long enough for intercourse. The prevalence of impotence in France was evaluated in a sample of 986 men aged 18 to 94 years. The overall prevalence was (published by Feldman and Smith) at their disposal containing normal (non erect) penis measurements. The first column of figures gives the average length, the second column shows the lower limit of what is considered to be 'normal'.

Age	Ave. length	Lower limit
Newborn 30 wks	2.5	1.5 cm
Newborn 40 wks	3.0	2.0 cm
Newborn at term	3.5	2.4 cm
0-5 months	3.9	1.9 cm
6-12 months	4.3	2.3 cm
1-2 years	4.7	2.6 cm
2-3 years	5.1	2.9 cm
3-4 years	5.5	3.3 cm
4-5 years	5.7	3.5 cm
5-6 years	6.0	3.7 cm
6-7 years	6.1	3.8 cm
7-8 years	6.2	3.7 cm
8-9 years	6.3	3.8 cm
9-10 years	6.3	3.8 cm
10-11 years	6.4	3.7 cm
Adults	13.3	9.3 cm

Little is known about the cause of a penis that is too small. Perhaps a shortage of male sex hormones in the last part of pregnancy plays a role. It can occur as a separate abnormality, or it can form part of a series of anatomical abnormalities.

Before deciding to perform an operation, it is important to talk first, preferably with a sexologist who has expertise in this area. This should be done in the light of the following rules:

■ The smaller the penis, the larger it becomes, in proportion, in erection;

- Only friction in the outer part of the vagina is important during coitus;
- The vagina can adapt itself to accommodate any size of penis;
- Thickness is more important than length;
- It is not a question of what he has got, but how he uses it;
- There is always someone worse off!

By keeping these rules in mind, the vast majority of men will be able to overcome any worries they may have about the length of their penis! In addition, there are a number of practical tips: do not wear jeans; do not wear underpants, boxer shorts are better; and trim your pubic hair if it is excessive.

If doubts remain, there are always the results of the scientific research published by the psychologist Fisher. He attempted to measure the effect of the size of the penis on sexual arousal in men and in women (students). In erotic stories, the penis was not described (control condition) or was described (experimental condition). In the description of the penis, the length was mentioned five times per story. Per story the length varied from small (7.5 cm), via average (12.5 cm), to large (20 cm). The study subjects were asked to judge their own level of arousal after reading one story, and they also had to say how aroused they thought the man and the woman in the story were. Afterwards, the subjects were asked whether they remembered the contents of the story; the control group obviously did not mention the length of the penis. The experimental group that had read about the largest penis, mentioned the length most often and there were no differences between the men and the women. The study subjects had apparently noticed the*nature* of the description, but were unable to say what the possible aim of the study might have been. In the judgements about their own level of arousal and that of the people in the story, the observed length of the penis did not play a role. 'Variation in the length of the penis does not appear to be a stipulation for arousal' the authors concluded.

The American psychologist Bernie Zilbergeld pointed out that men receives an unbelievable amount of benefit, at such little inconvenience'. In the same article, it said that it would not be long before the operation would be introduced in western Europe.

In August 1994, it was all set. A Dutch urologist told a national newspaper that he had ventured to perform the operation. 'It is a simple procedure. It took us a little more than two hours to do, at our ease, but it could be done in an hour and a half. It really gives a good result. The patient thought so too. He couldn't get enough of looking under the blankets. To him, I'm a hero.'

This news coverage caused great upheaval, not least owing to the poorly chosen words by the otherwise ever so friendly urologist: the hospital director, an influential professor of andrology, a famous cosmetic surgeon, board members of the Dutch Society of Urologists, a health ethicist, the chief editor of the *Gaykrant*, a representative from

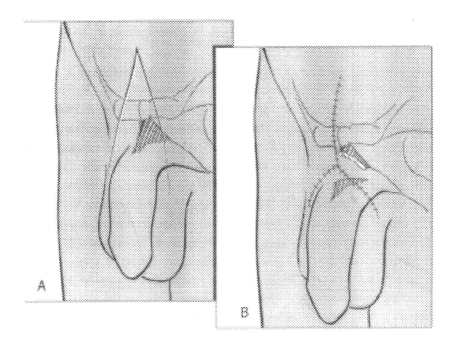

Figure 4: Penile lengthening

De Pinkeltjes, were all to have their say in various newspapers.

With the exception of the two latter persons, they all had serious objections. The andrologist was worried about the anatomical proportions: 'The questions is, will it go unpunished? By doing this, the suspension of the penis is changed. Is that wise? Maybe it will snap', were the words of the professor. The hospital director and the ethicist agreed that: 'In future, a medical ethics committee must always be asked first'. The poor urologist did not really understand the friction. 'At present, there is no reason at all to reject penis lengthening. Only the Chinese have produced publications about it. Let me do some research first; perform a series of operations and then publish the results'.

Unfortunately, not only the urologist in question, but also all those who had commented did not seem to have delved sufficiently into the scientific literature. The procedure is nothing more than a variation of an operation that has been known for many years and does not involve anything experimental. The essence of the intervention is that the ligament which fixes the penis to the front of the pubic bone - the suspensory ligament - is cut through. In this way, the 'hanging' part of the penis becomes longer. At the same time, the surgeon cuts the skin in such a way that it can also slide towards the penis. He then stitches the skin differently from how he has cut it. In jargon, this is called V-Y plasty. In other words, the incision has the form of a V, but after it has been stitched it forms a Y-shaped scar.

In addition, there are also ways to make the penis *thicker*, but that is a completely different story. One way is to transplant subcutaneous fat from the inside of the thighs.

Experts - paediatric urologists and sexologically - orientated urologists - have been in agreement for some time that: in men with a penis length of less than four centimetres (less than 7cm in erection), there can be a good reason to perform a penis lengthening procedure, obviously also on the advice of a sexologist. As a comparison, the average length of the penis of a newborn baby boy is three and a half cm. Since 1975, penis experts have had a scientifically-based table estimated to be 42%, with rates of 35% in men aged 18 to 35 years and 47% in those 36 to 94 years of age.

Owing to the fact that an erection not only affects the man, but also his (female) partner, a study was performed in America to answer the question of how women experience erectile problems in their partner. In the USA, between twenty and thirty million men suffer from impotence, but only one in twenty seeks medical help. Although the majority of American women were satisfied with their sexual life, 41% of the women with an impotent partner felt frustrated about the problem, 29% were disappointed and 18% were even angry. 4% were considering divorce. Almost half (!) felt responsible for their partner's problem, but the vast majority (80%) did not encourage their partner to seek (medical) help. The most remarkable of these findings was that apparently, the women were not willing to face up to the decreasing potency of their partner. This means that they were not going to take any initiative either.

It is clear that the risk of impotence increases with the years. Sexual needs decrease and the level of arousal decreases. The blood vessels start to lose their elasticity, physical complaints occur and more and more medication is taken that has a negative effect on potency.

What is the situation amongst immigrant men? Are they more prone to impotence? Do they deal differently with the problem? Almost half of the immigrant men in Holland come from Turkey or Morocco and the majority are Muslims. According to general practitioners, they often express sexual problems via a physical complaint. Erectile problems can be presented as 'penis pain', 'knee pain' or 'stomach ache'. An extensive physical examination is therefore very important. Presumably the complaint is presented under concealment, because within Islamic culture, it is taboo to talk about psychosocial and sexual problems with an outsider. In contrast, 'being ill' is perfectly acceptable. Usually, Turkish and Moroccan men expect treatment by means of medication. An injection is more highly thought of than a tablet, powder or suppository. Among Turkish men, potency and fertility play an important role in their feelings of self-esteem. Erectile problems, therefore, can be experienced as a loss of vitality or even as looming death. Problems arise if they are referred to a female specialist. It is difficult for Turkish men to see her as an expert; women are by definition subordinate to men.

Psychological or physical?

Not only the patients, but also the doctors find it important to find out whether impotence is caused by psychological or physical factors. Why is this? In a patient with, for example, a stomach ulcer, generally very little attention is paid to the psychosocial problems underlying the problem. A prescription for medication to neutralise the stomach acid quickly materialises. This is so-called symptomatic treatment. However, if a patient presents with impotence he is not let off the hook so easily. To the best of his or her abilities, the expert **must** investigate whether the problem is psychological or physical. This is probably one of the reasons why a lot of men are ashamed to come forward with erectile problems. Once he has seen his general practitioner, he will prefer to be referred to a urologist. He uses gadgets, syringes and needles, or might even perform an operation. Apparently, for many men that is less of a threat than having to talk to a sexologist and go into all sorts of details about the failure of his love life.

The patient can expect the following questions: Do you have problems getting or maintaining an erection? If erection occurs, then the blood supply is probably good. How long does your erection last? Does your erection disappear before or during coitus? How long have you been suffering from this complaint? Does it make a difference what position you take during coitus? Men are vulnerable in the 'missionary position', because as soon as they start making coital movements, relatively more blood is conducted away to their upper legs. This can occur at the cost of the circulation to the penis, particularly if the blood vessels are affected by arteriosclerosis. The English express this aptly by saying: 'It's a choice between sex or legs'.

Other questions to find out the cause for impotence are: Are there any physical complaints of another nature? Do you use medication, alcohol, tobacco, drugs, and if so how much? The psychosocial aspects are investigated thoroughly: Is your impotence associated with your partner? - how do you ask that question clearly and nevertheless discreetly? - or does tiredness play a role? Did something unpleasant happen when the problem occurred for the first time? How are you getting on at work and what are your career prospects? Do you have any worries that might unconsciously be demanding a great deal of your attention? Has something happened to your regular partner which has made him or her less attractive? Do you have erections at night or in the morning and is masturbation just as successful as it used to be? Do you still feel like having sex? How does the man view his situation and how is his sexual partner reacting to it?

During physical examination, it is important to establish whether the man has the normal male pattern of hair growth. A stethoscope is used to find out whether there are any signs of narrowing of the blood vessels, reflexes are tested and the penis, testicles and prostate are palpated. Physical examination of an impotent man does not usually uncover anything that he was not already well-aware of. Nevertheless a great many men believe that their impotence is the first sign of a serious disease. Unfortunately, this is occasionally the case. In young men it might indicate multiple sclerosis, while in elderly men it might indicate severe vascular disease or prostate cancer.

Other diseases which can lead to impotence are: persistent high blood pressure, leukaemia, severe kidney disease, over-activity or under-activity of the thyroid gland, diabetes, under-developed testicles or bilateral damage to the testicles, over-activity or under-activity of the pituitary gland, over-activity of the adrenal glands, amyotrophic lateral sclerosis (disease of the spinal cord), spinal cord lesion, severe epilepsy, slipped vertebral disc, Parkinson's disease and last but not least, inflammation of the prostate. Men who are suffering from the latter often complain of painful ejaculation.

If a patient has cancer and it is necessary to remove the prostate, bladder or large colon, this usually leads to impotence. This is associated with the fact that the urologist or surgeon has to remove a large amount of healthy tissue around the tumour in order to have a chance of curing the patient. In the process, he or she unavoidably damages nerves that are necessary for getting an erection. It is very important to warn the patient about this side-effect**before** the operation. Radiotherapy to the lower abdomen can also cause impotence.

Supplementary tests

Normally, every man has nocturnal erections. The duration and hardness depend on the man's age. Erections generally occur three to five times per night for ten to thirty minutes in connection with dream sleep. In the case of impotence with a physical cause, nightly erections occur occasionally if at all. A first indication of a man's erectile capacity can be established by means of having him wear an erection meter around his penis for several nights in succession. Such a meter is no more than a felt band marked with measurement graduations. The next morning, you can see whether nightly erections occurred and read off how much the circumference increased. Everyone can do the test themselves with the aid of the white edging paper around a sheet of postage stamps. The edging is formed into a ring and fitted loosely around the penis. If there are tears in the ring the next morning, then proof of nightly erections has more or less been established. University hospitals generally have more sophisticated equipment to record nightly erections. The doctor will want to record several details: whether nightly erections occur, how hard they are, how long they last and how large the increase in circumference was.

Sometimes erection measurements are performed while the patient is watching a porno film. In jargon this is called 'visual sexual stimulation'. It is a means of finding out whether erectile problems have a psychological cause.

Blood supply and drainage can be measured using *duplex scanning*. 'Duplex' means that two investigations are combined: ultrasound and doppler. Duplex measurements are performed at 'rest' and after an intrapenile injection (i.e. an injection into the penis) of a vasodilatory agent. Ultrasound can localise the arteries in the penis and doppler can measure the speed of the blood flow. If the blood supply is seriously disturbed in a young man, then it might be worthwhile to perform by-pass surgery to the penis. This form of surgery is not performed very often in Holland. Usually, it is not a case of insufficient blood supply, but of venous leakage. The erectile bodies of the penis cannot retain the blood sufficiently.

To form a better idea about this leakage, sometimes dynamic cavernosography is performed. During the test, a needle is inserted into the erectile bodies and a contrast agent is injected. In this way, the leak can be detected. If necessary it can be closed surgically.

A minority of impotent men seek the cause for their complaint on a psychological level. Grief after the loss of a loved one is encountered fairly often, particularly in widowers who after a time, want to start a new relationship. The same problem also applies to widows or divorced women who are trying to start again. They too have to wait and see whether they hit it off sexually. Problems arise when both 'new' partners expect (perhaps unjustly) to share their bed with the other at the earliest possible opportunity. Then the widower is expected to be potent. First, he has taken care of his wife for many years, then she dies and then he falls into a deep, dark hole. The same obviously applies to the widow. Sybren Polet describes that a new sexual relationship can be successful in older age, in *Droom van de Oplichter: werkelijkheid* (Dream of the Swindler: Truth):

> *That looks like a sheep, what you've got there between your legs, he said.*
> *Do you think I've got too much hair?*
> *No, it's just right, nice and full, I like that. My ex-wife also had a lot of hair.*
> *You are not going to start taking about your ex-wife are you?*
> *No, he said, let bygones be bygones. Come here.*
> *[...]*
> *Get 'em off then, she said, you're being shy.*

I haven't done it for three and a half years, he said embarrassed, and before that, after my wife died, it only happened a couple of times.

Did you get many letters?

Quite a lot. But I didn't go to bed with anyone. There wasn't really much chance one way or another. But with you it was different right away.

Most men want to climb between the sheets within a quarter of an hour, she said.

Yes, I know, but I'm not like that.

I don't know, she said, I wouldn't do it otherwise.

She climbed beside him into a double bed.

Did you wash your little man?

Yes, of course, I always do. I like to keep myself clean.

[...]

Shall we then?

Yes, she said, come on then.

He rolled on top of her, fumbled about clumsily until his penis finally slipped inside, and then let out a sigh of relief.

Some men use an aid, she said, or a sort of harness if it doesn't stay hard long enough.

I don't need one of those, he said, at least not yet.

[...]

And suddenly it was as though his penis shot through her with the speed of a snake: it grew longer and longer, wriggled and sniffed with its globular head into all the nooks and crannies of her body, stomach, throat, buttocks, thighs, feet and even via her shoulders, into her arms and hands. It was a mad but highly exciting experience. Soon his penis shrunk abruptly, aware of its mistake. With a last thrust he ejaculated, without taking the opportunity to ask her whether she was ready, too.

Unfortunately, for many widows and widowers, starting a new relationship does not always go as easily as the one described by Polet.

Impotence at a young age is usually an expression of shyness. It is only occasionally caused by a serious psychological problem. A.F.Th. van der Heijden wrote about this in his novel *De Gevaren-driehoek* (1992) (The Warning Triangle). The central figure, Albert, starts a relationship with Milli, a rather inhibited law student. Sadly, they do not manage to achieve sexual contact that is satisfying for both parties. In Albert's case, the suggestion of a family relationship between them and feelings of shame play a negative role. However, after careful research, Milli finds out that they are not related. She becomes convinced that Albert is impotent. He is, too, but he does not dare to admit it. Albert is labelled a coward. He is at his wits' end. He finds the solution with a girl called Marieke, who has unintentionally become pregnant. Albert pays for her abortion that was conceived by someone else. In return she promises to help him overcome his impotence. To their regret, they do not manage this before the abortion, but a few days afterwards. A fragment:

> *Not only had he managed to penetrate her deeply without using any force, but now that she was enveloping him , he felt... nothing. Before he could become embedded, her soft lining billowed away from him. The thumbscrew that he had feared, appeared to be a hollow, powerless fist, that with its sticky palm could not get a grip on him, on the contrary, it seemed to weaken more and more.*

A bit further on:

> *For the first time in his almost twenty-two years, he ejaculated his seed into the deeper folds of a woman's body. It was a lukewarm orgasm, that did not give him any relief. As ejaculation with a partly soft penis is sometimes painful, he was even left with a slightly chafed feeling.*
>
> *When he pulled his rolled-up foreskin forward again - to lessen the irritation - Albert felt a strange stickiness, which could not be the result of their combined fluids. He rubbed his fingertips together.*

They stuck. He put the light on.... Blood. Diluted blood. On his hands, on the sheets, between her legs, where the stiff hair was peaked together into little spit-curls.

Impotence can also be caused by young ladies. Some of them are easily distracted during love-making, they become bored (it's not really as exciting as they expected) or start to display feelings of protest. Their subsequent disparaging and sometimes insulting remarks can cause their lover's penis to wilt. This is particularly likely to occur if the man involved was thinking that he needed to give a really splendid performance, while he is feeling insecure. Sometimes he might be afraid of hurting his partner, or he might believe that the virginal membrane is like the skin on a drum - a closed and highly taut membrane that, with an enormous amount of pain, has to be bored through at the first coitus.

In addition, he might also be suffering from anxiety about his own genital organ. One of the most common expressions of this is that the man has never learnt to wash his penis properly, including exposing the glans. If, with a strong erection, and even more when penetrating a narrow vaginal opening, his foreskin rolls back from the glans, then he will feel a little pain and a great deal of terror. The result is that he immediately stops at the first advance and does not make any further attempts at coitus.

If during a medical consultation the patient does not mention this spontaneously and just says that he can get a good erection, but that it wilts as soon as it enters the vagina, then there is plenty of reason to perform a physical examination. The man is asked to pull back his foreskin. Sometimes it looks as though he is doing his best, but he fails nevertheless. When one offers to help, this is waved aside. After some persuasion and not without great anxiety, he usually lets the doctor expose his glans. Very often the man involved has nearly fainted. A considerable amount of smegma is evidence that personal hygiene of the foreskin is lacking. Subsequently, the man is encouraged to pull back his foreskin everyday and to wash underneath with soap and water. This is the quickest way for him to overcome his anxiety about the vulnerability of his exposed glans. If all goes well, he will no longer find it difficult to entrust his precious organ to the folds of his partner.

Not only rancour about one's partner having an (extramarital) affair, but also an affair itself can sometimes lead to impotence. An Italian feminist, Pia Fontana, wrote about impotence in *The Diary*. In the story she describes that Elsa seduces the married cardiologist, Riccardo. They had made each other's acquaintance at a friend's house, after which she had made an appointment to see him at his practice, not because of an ailment, but with other intentions. It takes until the second consultation for Riccardo to realise what is going on. Elsa manages to arouse him terribly, but she also realises that making love between the customary metal filing cabinet, a folding screen with wrinkled material, an examination table with a strip of protective white paper covering it, with on his desk the unavoidable photo of his wife and two children, would be an awful experience. Elsa goes exploring and discovers a bathroom with little blue tiles. This is where it will have to happen, she thinks, and turns on the hot tap:

He stroked her, lay on top of her, and then something embarrassing happened - embarrassing for him - Elsa did not find it so strange: despite everything, Riccardo could not get it up. Well, it's not exceptional, but it is tiresome, for both of them... He tried, tried again and still he could not manage. And he really wanted to, perhaps too much, or perhaps there was something else.

Elsa becomes irritated by his failure and Riccardo keeps apologising and saying that she must have cast a spell on him:

Why do you keep on trying? asked Elsa. You don't have to bother on my account, you know! They dried themselves off with strips of white paper - the stuff on the examination table - there was a whole roll of it in the cupboard.

As Elsa leaves the practice she thinks that he is nevertheless a nice and interesting man. She smiles at the thought of his failed attempt, but he does not get a second chance.

Divorce and stress at work are also well-known causes of impotence, just as concealed homosexuality. In America it is estimated that between the two and four million people are married to a homosexual or bisexual partner - usually without knowing. 20 to 35% of American lesbians and homosexuals marry, although they should really have known better. 95% of married homosexuals were aware of their own sexual preference before they got married and 90% had already had homosexual contacts. The majority believed that marriage would 'cure' them. After a husband had admitted his homosexuality, 15% of these American couples stayed together, according to a recent American newspaper article.

An illustrative example from clinical practice: a fifty-three-year-old, well-groomed man made an appointment at the outpatient clinic because he had erectile problems. His general physical condition was good, although he had diabetes and needed two insulin injections per day. Diabetes suggested a physical cause for his complaints, but not every complaint from a diabetic patient is a consequence of the illness. The patient had been married for nineteen years - according to him happily. After a number of tests had been performed, it appeared that the problem was not so much his getting an erection, but his becoming sexually aroused. The man had been fostering homosexual feelings for many years, but did not want to put them into practice. There was not a hair on his head that would consider divorcing his wife. He was living in a somewhat isolated, small village. According to him, *coming out* about his feeling was totally impossible. The patient was not keen on the idea of talking to a psychologist-sexologist. The suggestion of secretly making homosexual contacts in the nearby city was also rejected. He did make it clear that he wished to be followed-up at the clinic.

The basis for this wish did not become clear to me until I had talked to another homosexual. He explained that the man involved might view consulting a male urologist as a sort of 'sexual' contact. In any case, it gave him the opportunity to talk openly and freely about his feelings.

During the course of history, some political leaders are known to have had potency problems when they were involved in a power struggle, particularly while they were waiting for the result. Mao Zedong was one of them. 'When he became very powerful at the beginning of the nineteen sixties, he seldom complained of impotence', said his personal physician in a biography about the great leader. At a very young age, Mao had decided to grow old in good health and to remain sexually active into his eighties. But pride goes before a fall. His personal physician had to give him regular injections containing an extract of ground deer antler which, according to traditional Chinese medicine, was an aphrodisiac. And naturally, they did not help!

Just like Mao, the majority of men with potency problems think that there is something wrong with them physically. Not being able to get an erection is considered to be equivalent to being ill. Firstly, the man will want to have a physical examination. His penis is offered for cure or repair. Preferably with pills or injections, possibly with an operation by the urologist who, from time immemorial, is the plumber among surgeons. The man never asks himself why he is impotent. The present issue is: What is wrong with my body and can you cure the disorder? It is only very rarely that a man who cannot get an erection says, 'Seems logical to me; I have no desire for sex'.

In the nineteen eighties, the American psychologist Bernie Zilbergeld was considered to be an expert in the field of male sexuality. In his books, he sketches the still valid picture of the penis with his skilful pen: 'It's two feet long, hard as steel, and can go all night'. To support this statement, he frequently cites from the popular literature, for example, from *The Giants* by Harold Robbins:

Tenderly her fingers opened his uniform and he sprang forward as a ferocious lion from his cage. Carefully she pulled his foreskin back so that his red vicious glans became visible, and she took him in both hands, one against the other, as though she was holding a baseball bat. She stared at it unbelievingly. 'C'est formidable. Un vrai canon.'

It is through accounts like these that many men become terrified creatures, whose penis does not always behave like a cross between a baseball bat, a ferocious lion and a canon!

Occasionally a man admits that his impotence has something to do with his partner. He is bored with her. There is no curiosity, there are no more secrets. The excitement is gone. Being in a rut is the cause of this impotence. In this respect, apparently not only the vagina, but also the penis has the right to go on strike. Sexologists call this the Coolidge phenomenon. The name stems from the American president Calvin Coolidge. According to the anecdote, the president and his wife spend a day on a farm. The president and his wife split up for the programme and Mrs Coolidge inspects the chicken runs. She asks the farmer how often a cockerel copulates. 'Dozens of times a day, milady', the farmer answers. 'Please will you also tell the president that?' asks Mrs Coolidge. When it is the president's turn to inspect the chickens and the farmer tells him about the cockerel, he asks, 'Everyday with the same chicken?' 'Oh no, sir! Every time with a different one.' Coolidge nods his head and says, 'Please will you tell my wife that?'

Always having sexual contact with the same partner also has its advantages. In 1994 the psychologist Zeegers published *De zonnige zijde van seks; de nawerking van positief beleefde seksualiteit* (The sunny-side of sex: the after-effects of positively experienced sexuality). In his book he compares the sex lives of married couples and divides them into three sorts: couples who always do the same things in bed, couples who make something special of it every time and couples who invite other people to share their bed. These couples were selected on the basis of various criteria, including their own opinion that they have a satisfying sexual relationship.

It is hardly surprising that the various couples experienced sexuality differently. However, the degree to which their experiences of sex differed was very interesting. In the couples with little variety, everything always went well. None of the times they made love ever stood out. It obviously never occurred to them that it might sometimes be a bit boring. They never fantasized during love-making. In this group the elements of love and intimacy were certainly present. Moreover, one partner always knew that the other would never do anything strange. Very reliable. In the other two groups there were obviously ups and downs and their sex lives were much more exciting.

Cultural influences

The way people view impotence has everything to do with the time and culture in which they live. The ancient Chinese, for example, never considered the phenomenon of impotence to be a major problem. According to Jolan Chang in his book *The Tao of Love and Sex*, if the penis was not hard enough for penetration, the method of 'soft penetration' (Ancient Chinese squeeze technique) was advised. If a man had enough experience, he would even be able to manoeuvre a completely flaccid penis into the vagina by using this ancient Chinese technique. Soft penetration might prove to be a new and arousing experience for the woman.

According to the tao, a man should not attempt soft penetration if the vagina is not already moist. If necessary, vegetable oil can be used for lubrication. The key to the success of the soft penetration technique is the dexterity of the man's fingers. As soon as the penis has been manoeuvred into the vagina, he must use his fingers to form a ring around the base of his penis. The aim is to make the tip of the penis as hard as possible.

It might be concluded that soft penetration is a useful technique for men with erectile problems, but that potent men will not feel the need to use it. In Chinese tradition, this is not true. Jolan Chang writes: 'Soft penetration is not just aimed at the beginner or someone with a problem, it forms an integrated part of the tao of love.' However, there is a catch. Soft penetration and the postponement of ejaculation only serve the man's self-interest. As prescribed in the tao, men who want to live a long life must replenish their gradually weakening yang - the essence of the man that is his source of strength, energy and longevity - with yin shui: the water of yin, or in other words the vaginal secretions of young women. As yang is essential to the health and energy of the man, he must not do anything to harm it. Therefore, a taoist seldom ejaculates during coitus. Instead, he tries to use the secretions of his female partners to maintain his strength. The more yin shui he absorbs, the more vital he becomes. It is therefore necessary to have coitus very frequently!

In the ancient Hindu culture, from about 4000 to 1000 years B.C., a cure for impotence was not so much sought within the man himself, but outside him. For example, he had to eat a mixture of sesame seeds, salt, pepper, brown sugar, eggs and buttermilk. The Hindus knew many remedies for impotence. These were set out in the Ayur-vedas, literally translated as: 'The knowledge of longevity'. The best known ayurveda are the *Sushruta* and *Caraka Samhitas*.

In the Indian sex handbook, *Kama Sutra*, written in 400 A.D., extensive attention is paid to the size of the genital organs. On the basis of the size of the penis, men are divided into hares, bulls and stallions. A woman can be a deer, a mare or an elephant. The *Kama Sutra* states that a combination of a hare-man and a deer-woman leads to better sex than a combination of one of these with a larger animal. Anyone who wishes to follow this advice will soon run into practical problems: how many partners will you need to try out before you find one who is the correct size?

In ancient India, a man with erectile weakness or a small penis was treated with ointment. The ingredients and method were as follows: equal parts of Rakta-bol powder (myrrh), Manashil (arsenic), Costus arabicus (aniseed) and Boric acid; mix the ingredients with sesame oil and keep applying the ointment to the penis until the desired result is achieved.

The Bible also speaks of impotence. In Kings I, King David is old and tired, so he is brought a young Sunamitic virgin in the hope that she will revive his zest. To the disappointment of his subjects, this ploy is unsuccessful. In Old testament language, the King does not 'know' her, i.e. he does not have intercourse with her. He is no longer capable of conceiving offspring. There are no more prospects. Even King David is not immortal.

When King Frederick II from Prussia, many centuries later, was lying weakened from old age on his deathbed, he too was prescribed a young virgin by his personal physician. In this case, it did not have anything to do with impotence. The doctor believed that the spirit of a young person could pass into an older person and bring about a sort of 'rebirth'. At that time this was referred to as 'sunamatism'. This belief was not only held by Western cultures. It was said that the legendary first emperor of China, the Yellow Emperor, progenitor of the tribe of Han and the man from whom all Chinese are thought to originate, was immortal because he went to bed with a thousand young virgins. The emperors who followed him also believed that the more sex partners they had, the longer they would live. This is why they had so many thousands of concubines.

Nowadays, the general opinion is that the refreshing effect that young people have on old people is chiefly psychological. Sometimes a young woman feels sexually attracted to an older man. This can even take on such proportions that people view it as an abnormality. Not so long ago, psychologists started to call this gerontophilia (desiring sexual relations with old people), but fortunately, people are no longer willing to accept such denigratory designations.

Impotence in the Middle Ages
In the middle ages, witches were often accused of causing impotence. For example, they were believed to be capable of casting spells on a man's penis so that it would withdraw completely into his abdomen. Particularly German witches were considered to be well-practised in the art. In effect, this was a form of Koro. Apparently it is a deeply-rooted, archaic fear. The first to connect impotence to witchcraft was

Hincmar, archbishop of Reims in the ninth century. One of his pronunciations was that a man was not permitted to remarry after a divorce on the grounds of proven impotence with a physical cause. However, if his impotence was caused by witchcraft, the victim was permitted to remarry.

Witches were also accused of having sexual relations with the devil. One problem was that the devil's penis differed strongly from that of a normal man. Some witches said that it was double-headed, forked and had the sinuosity of a snake's tongue. He was therefore able to penetrate a woman's vagina and anus simultaneously.

Other peculiarities were also ascribed to the devil's penis. For instance, according to the sexologist Coen van Emde Boas, there were stories about a penis with scales and barbs. Views about the length of the penis varied widely: from pinkie-finger length to the length of an arm. Besides the form, the composition of the penis was also described as deviant: it was ice cold, as hard as stone, half of horn or iron.

It is self-evident that sexual contact with such an organ would be very painful for the witch. It caused 'diabolical pain'. No, coitus with the devil was no fun at all! Mating with the prince of darkness was thought to produce more and more new witches and increased his power accordingly. The Middle ages teemed with nightmares and whore devils, demons disguised as a man or woman that crept into someone's bed and copulated with monks and virgins, servants and mistresses.

Generally, the publication of *Die Hexenkammer* (1487) is considered to be the beginning of 'real' witch hunting, while in fact, the persecution had started much earlier. In the book by two inquisitors, something is said about a man whose penis was spirited away by witchcraft, a case that could nowadays be considered as an example of temporary psychological impotence. Briefly, the story went as follows: after he had broken up with his girlfriend, the young man 'lost' his penis. Where his penis should have been, his body was completely smooth. Thereupon, he met a woman at an inn, who asked him why he was so unhappy. Her advice was, if necessary using force, to demand that the young lady in question return his penis.

He followed this advice and asked his ex-girlfriend to break the spell. When she expressed her innocence, he almost strangled her and said: 'If you don't give me my penis back, I will kill you'. The girl was intelligent enough to play along with the game. She put her hand between his thighs and said: 'Here, now you have it back'. From that moment, the young man could see and feel his penis in the correct place. The psychological cause of the impotence is quite clear. However, the inquisitors explained the mystery in their own way: the penis had not been torn from his body, but magicked away by the devil.

In his book *De Praestigiis Daemonum* (The Prestigious Demon) published in 1563, the Dutch author Johannes Weyer was one of the first to criticise witch hunting. Impotence was also mentioned. He emphasized that impotence usually has a 'natural' cause, for example it could be the consequence of eating certain herbs. In his opinion, if a man is suffering from impotence he should not make assumptions about magic spells or make accusations against innocent people.

Weyer did not deny that the devil could do harm to a man's reproductive capabilities, but he strongly stressed that Satan certainly would not need the help of old women. Neither did he have any time for all the stories about miraculous cures for impotence. When he heard about a man who had become potent again after rubbing himself with raven bile, Weyer concluded that superstition could not only harm a person, but apparently also be of benefit to him.

One should admire the psychological insight of this man, who was able to put an end to the nonsense, not by saying that the devil was fictitious, but by taking him seriously and hammering it home that he had made enormous fools of everyone with his lies about witchcraft. According to Weyer, it was not the women who were accused of witchcraft that were under the devil's spell, but the accusers themselves. A sublime statement, which saved the lives of hundreds of innocent women.

By studying a fifteenth century medical manuscript found in French Montpelier, the medical historian Sigerist uncovered an interesting discourse about impotence. In it he read - among other things - that some people were unable to have coitus because they had been cursed by the devil. If this happened to a man, he should open himself to God who would have mercy on him. Owing to the fact that there were various types of curse, it was considered necessary by the author of the manuscript, to deal with each of them separately.

Some curses involved the use of animal substances, such as cockerel testicles. If these were mixed with the cockerel's blood and put under the marital bed, it would be impossible for the couple to have sexual relations. Another method was to split a nut or an acorn into two halves and to hide them along the route the bridal couple would take after the wedding feast. Another sort of curse utilized hidden letters written in bat's blood. Sometimes raw beans were used and the effect was greatest when they were thrown onto the roof or placed above the door opening.

If bride or bridegroom was afflicted by one of these curses, then it was better for them to talk about it than to remain silent. Otherwise they would not only disgrace themselves, but also their families and they would sin in the face of the Holy Ghost. Here are four, freely translated, remedies:

A curse by letters can be recognised by the fact that the bridegroom and bride do not hold each other dear. A search must be made both above and below the door opening, and if anything is found it must be taken directly to the bishop or priest. If a nut or an acorn is the cause, then the woman must split a nut or acorn into two halves, each must take one half in their hand, stand on opposite sides of the road from each other, walk towards each other and join the two halves together for at least seven days. Afterwards they will be able to have coitus. If the curse has been laid by means of beans, then it is only possible to lift it with the help of God. [...]

The bile of a dog purifies the home and makes it immune to further curses. If the walls are sprinkled with the dog's blood, then the curses will be lifted. If the bride and groom collect bile from fish and keep it in a basket made of twigs from a juniper bush and scatter it onto the hearth-fire in the evening, this will also lift the curses.

If these remedies did not work, they had to seek the help of a priest. After going to confession, the married couple were offered Holy Communion on Easter morning or on Ascension day. After receiving the Body and Blood of Christ, it was the intention that the couple give each other the Kiss of Reconciliation. Then they were blessed and sent on their way with the firm advice to abstain from any attempts at coitus for three days and three nights. After this period, it was bound to work!

Doctors and medical students are not famous for exceptional sexual performance, at least not according to women of experience. However, they do have excuses for this: too busy, irregular hours, great emotional stress from their work, etc. The story was the same in the Middle Ages. At that time there was even a poem with a double meaning about impotence among doctors. The literary man, Hans van Straten dug it up. It was about a lady patient with a deep wound, who wished to have it probed and anointed by her kind doctor. His jar of ointment failed to perform to requirements and she announced that he would be better off repairing shoes than trying to seduce a woman.

Nicolas Famel (1330-1418), a famous scholar at the University of Paris, was both exorcist and alchemist. In his opinion rotting wood was extremely effective against impotence, but the wood did have to be soaked first for three days in the urine of a sixteen-year-old virgin. Another of his remedies was:

Take some pappus seed; put it into a bowl; add the left testicle of a three-year-old goat, a pinch of powder made from the hair of a perfectly white dog that was cut off on the first day of the new moon and burnt on the seventh. Pour the mixture into a bottle half filled with brandy; let it stand, uncorked for 21 days so that the stars can do their work.

On the twenty-first day, the first day of the next new moon, boil the liquid until it becomes a thick syrup; then add four drops of crocodile semen and pour the mixture through a muslin cloth.

    After collecting the liquid in a dish, all you have to do is rub it into the affected parts of the impotent man, and subsequently, he will do wonders. The mixture is so effective, that even by only using it secretly, women become pregnant.

    As crocodiles are very rare in this country and as it is very difficult to obtain semen from these creatures, the semen from certain breeds of dog can be used. According to Cleopatra, this is possible because dogs are so adept at avoiding the greedy jaws of crocodiles. These creatures are very common along the banks of the River Nile. In any case, the above experiment has been repeated many times and it has always been successful, with canine semen as well as with crocodile semen.

Castration

According to legend, man copied castration from the hyena. It is said of these animals that shortly after the offspring are born, the father singles out the males and bites off their testicles, probably to combat future competition. In human males, fear of castration runs deep, deeper than most men think. In Greek mythology, several references are made to it, for instance in the story about Uranus and in the one about Melampus. Venus arose from the vital parts of Uranus that were thrown into the sea. Melampus was later involved in curing the king's son of impotence. This impotence was caused by fear of castration.

    In the ancient Hindu tradition, physicians did what many present day urologists consider to be the best therapy for metastasized prostate cancer, namely chemical castration. Nowadays this is accomplished with expensive pills, whereas in those days a cheap diet was prescribed: vegetarian. It contained far too little cholesterol, which in the human body is a base material for testosterone. That is how they did it. Castration eases the path to total sexual abstinence, which leaves more energy for spiritual purposes. In the meantime, scientific research has shown that a low-fat diet reduces the testosterone level in the blood by about ten per cent.

In ancient Rome, castration was also a well-known phenomenon. The Romans distinguished between four different types: real *castrati* - removal of both testicles and the penis; *spadones* - removal of the testicles; *thlibiae* - destroying the testicles by crushing; and *thlasiae* - severing the spermatic cords. Naturally, this only applied to slaves.

Ultimately, castration was done on such a large scale that the emperor was obliged to forbid it. Not physicians, but barbers or attendants at bath houses conducted the procedure. They were paid by slave traders and brothel keepers. Initially, it was a slave trader's right to deal in eunuchs. After the prohibition, the priests of Cybele still continued to mutilate themselves. And not only themselves, but also any unfortunate lads that happened to fall into their hands. People called them *galli*, in other words capons, castrated cockerels. They were destined for a job in prostitution.

At the time of the Byzantine kingdom, it had been noticed that castrated men were less competitive and less aggressive than men with testicles. Many of these unfortunates became civil servants. People could take them at their word and they did as they were told. They knew their place and did not form a threat to the emperor and his paladins.

Over the course of centuries, farmers have realised that castrating their animals can be very beneficial. They were easier to fatten-up and a gelding was much easier to handle than a stallion.

According to the annals of the Zwolse monastery Windesheim, impotence by one's own hand was not uncommon in the Middle Ages. On 23 August 1451, Nicolaas van Cusa, as papal legate, granted the priors at all the Windesheim monasteries permission 'to bury any subordinates that castrated themselves or otherwise mutilated themselves and died of the consequences, in secret and outside the graveyard'. Apparently, church authority had realised that self-castration was not a sign of faith. Therefore, eunuchs were literally and figuratively heaped together with witches, deviationists, the poor and mentally insane.

In the fourth century A.D., there were men within the sect of the

Obelites that had themselves castrated on the grounds of a text from the *Bible* (*Matthew* 19:12):

For here are some eunuchs which were so born from their mother's womb; and there are some eunuchs which were made eunuchs of men; and there be eunuchs which have made themselves for the Kingdom of heaven's sake. He that is able to recieve it, let him receive it.

Strangely enough, they did not condemn marriage, but they did condemn sexual intercourse. Two centuries earlier, in about 120 A.D, a gnostic sect appeared in the Near East, the Adamists, who believed that they could create paradise by suppressing all sensual desires. In imitation of Adam, they walked around naked during their religious ceremonies.

Many centuries later, in the eighteenth century, it was common practice in the Russian-Romanian sect of the Skopzen, not only to remove the testicles, but also to remove the major portion of the penis after having children. Initially this was done with red-hot iron rods. It was not until later that knives were used. People called the scars the 'Large Holy Seal'. If the penis remained intact, the scars were called the 'Small Holy Seal'. (See figure overleaf)

The sect arose from a group of flagellants. The female sect members did not mutilate their ovaries, but their labia, breasts and nipples.

All this excrescence undoubtedly sprang from early Christian beliefs about martyrdom, including the accompanying physical abstinence, self-punishment and hardships as the only way to salvation.

In the seventeenth and eighteenth centuries, not only the organisers of the operas, but also the Catholic Church made grateful use of lads that had been castrated at a young age. If, in those days, you were a ten-year-old boy in Italy, with any kind of singing voice and you were from a poor family, then there was a good chance that with the intervention of the parish priest, you would be press-ganged. This meant that before

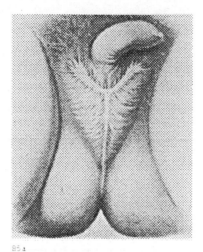

Das kleine „heilige" Siegel

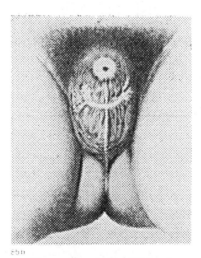

Das große „heilige" Siegel
der Kastratensekten

Figure 5: 'Small Holy Seal' / 'Large Holy Seal'

your voice had broken, you would be castrated by coarse means. The testicles were immersed in boiling water, after which they withered. Subsequently, the larynx did not develop, while the rest of the body did. The effect of a 'broken voice' was thus irrevocably prevented. After puberty, the unfortunate castrato had a small larynx with a large thorax on top, which he naturally could fill with a large quantity of air. He could then force the air out through relatively small vocal cords. In this way, he retained his high boy's voice and could sing soprano roles in adulthood.

The boy and his parents were promised free training for him as an opera singer, including the potential of a later singing career. However, just as it is today, many were called, but few were chosen. There was very little chance of following a career in opera or obtaining a steady position as a singer in the Sistine chapel. Anyone who did not succeed had to make do with a humble existence as a priest or something similar. The price he had to pay? He would spend the rest of his life with a tendency towards becoming fat, his penis would remain small and his prostate and seminiferous tubules would not develop. He would not develop the male pattern of hair growth and would not have to shave. He would not go bald either and however long he lay in the sun, he would not become tanned.

There is no agreement about the precise whys and wherefores of castration. The most logical explanation is that in those days, women were not allowed to perform on stage. Castratos played the female roles. Another explanation is based on the artistic notion that a castrato possesses the triad of male and female sensuality and childish beauty. This notion also links up with the ancient Greek ideal of androgynia: the union of manhood and womanhood.

Castratos were the pop idols of their time. If a castrato was successful, he attained a nearly godly status. In Italy, a successful castrato voice was called a *canaro elefante*: a canary's voice in an elephant's body.

Sensational stories circulated about the sexual encounters of and with castratos. They were always sterile, but not always impotent.

Moreover, they exhibited a certain tenderness. In a time without contraceptives, this was an attractive combination for a woman!

Unfortunately, only one recording remains of a castrato, which dates from the beginning of this century. It is probable that this recording - recently released by EMI on the CD *Le temps des castrates* - is not representative. The singer, Alessandro Moreschi, was already elderly and was certainly not one of the best.

Impotence and law suits

Church Father Augustine (354-430) was probably one of the first to declare that sexual intercourse should always occur with the hope of conception. 'Go forth and multiply', as it says in the Biblical book of *Genesis*. Impotent men could not do that and violated the sacrament of marriage. It was as simple as that!

In accordance with Augustine, church law from the thirteenth century onwards considered it to be a more or less deadly sin for an impotent man to get married. Such a man could be brought before the church court. The French historian Pierre Darmon wrote that in the lower classes, it was usually the neighbours who took the initiative to institute legal proceedings, while in the higher classes the wife was usually the petitioner. The goal was to receive damages, as if they had been sold a lame horse. Older women used impotence law suits to wage feuds over an inheritance, while younger women seized the opportunity to take revenge for sexual difficulties or relationship problems. In some cases the husband would start counter-proceedings as the next step in a series of sordid affairs.

Charges were also brought against men with undescended testicles. Doctor Goeury-Duvidier gave the following example in his *Gids voor lijders en lijderessen aan ziekten der urine - en geslachtswerktuigen* (1921) (Guide for male and female sufferers from urinary and genital illnesses):

Sebastiaan Rouillard, one of the most learned lawyers from the parliament of Paris, pleaded in favour of a certain nobleman in the year 1600, who was accused by his wife of being impotent. She had won her case with the official of Sens and with the delegate of the primatie of Lyon.

The accused appealed against their verdict and received commissioners from the holy apostolic chair to decide the case as a last resort. Rouillard, his lawyer, made one statement, in which he proved that a man born without visible testicles, but with the other male characteristics, was perfectly capable of performing his marital duties. The nobleman had been born with this deformity, and it was on these grounds that his wife accused him of being impotent. He insisted that he had had sexual intercourse, not using the ridiculous means that she assumed, but in the natural manner of his sex.

The parliament of Paris passed judgement: without two visible testicles, a man was not permitted to marry.

Since the sixteenth century, the number of impotence law suits has gradually increased. Many thousands of court records have been circulated. The accused became the victim of satirical poems and was ridiculed in public.

During the trial, the accused had to prove by whatever means that he could get a stiff erection. A jury comprising theologists, doctors and midwives judged the result. The court records show that if necessary, the members of the jury sat at the accused's bedside at night in order to judge the possible emergence of a nightly erection. The pompous rituals surrounding these impotence law suits indirectly confirmed the power of the Catholic church. Initially, there was some degree of discretion, but in the course of the sixteenth century, the church authorities shifted sharply from spiritual voyeurism to actual voyeurism. By this time, they not only required a demonstration of the stiff erection, but also of its 'elasticity and natural movement'. Sometimes the jury also insisted on having a demonstration of ejaculation. Naturally, as time went by this was not enough either, and the married couple had to have sexual intercourse in the presence of the jury, a so-called 'congress'.

The most tragic trial was that of René de Cordouan, Marquis of Langey. After his wife, Marie de Saint-Simon, had made her accusation, the whole of Paris buzzed with rumours. To begin with, the majority decision of the jury was that there was nothing wrong with the Marquis' penis. Moreover, in Marie de Saint-Simon's case, absolutely nothing more of the hymen was visible. Nevertheless, the people continued to harbour doubts. For this reason, the Marquis insisted on having a 'congress'. Angry tongues claimed that 'apparently his fingers had been put to good use'.

On the big day, fifteen experts were present. The trial took place at the public baths. The Marquis had thought the matter through carefully. He insisted that his wife should first take a hot bath so that if she had used any astringents, these would be washed away. Her hair had to be loose so that no charms could be hidden in it. To his amazement, he was not able to get an erection while they were together. He kept trying for four hours before he gave up. On 8 February 1659, their marriage was dissolved.

Physical examination of the accused and his wife was an important element in impotence law suits. In itself this was nothing new. Even in Roman times the young couple were examined before they got married. At the end of the sixteenth century, genital function examinations became a subject for debate. According to the feminist Bernadette de Wit in a review of Darmon's book, 'People shrugged their shoulders about erection tests, but as far as the examination of "female modesty" was concerned, prudish indignation was mixed with hardly concealed lust.'

Whatever the accuser did, she compromised herself. If she remained married to an impotent man, then she was also guilty of violating the sacrament. If on the other hand, she took action, then she was suspected of having knowledge that a decent woman was not supposed to have. After dissolving her marriage, the only thing she could do was enter the convent. Who should we pity most, the woman or her husband? It was not until 1677 that the Church of Rome dispensed

The Secret Part 99

with impotence law suits.

In the last chapter of his book, Darmon wonders how it could have ever come to impotence law suits. Possibly the initiative came from inquisitive doctors and lawyers who could not believe that a man with a normal build could be impotent. Their occupational misconduct was not corrected in any manner at all. The church was more than willing to participate, because it formed a means of displaying power, while at first the public found the proceedings highly amusing. Undoubtedly the obsessive discussions about impotence and other sexual abnormalities served as an outlet for suppressed sexual feelings.

Medication

Over a century ago, people began to realised that certain types of medication could cause impotence. Roubaud described how he treated tuberculosis with iodine vapours and saw four cases of impotence occur. He found 'strong emaciation of the testicles'. Saltpetre also gained a bad reputation. The use of bromide compounds chiefly led to a decrease in sexual desire. Camphor inhibited the 'sensitivity of the genital tract'.

Nowadays particularly blood pressure medication and psychopharmaceuticals have a bad name in this respect. The same also applies to a number of medications for heart arrhythmia, Parkinson's disease, certain medications to counteract excessive stomach acid and some drugs for the treatment of prostate cancer. Some of these have a negative influence on a person's desire for sex, while others inhibit erection of the cavernous bodies of the penis or lead to 'dry orgasm', i.e. the semen is ejaculated into the bladder. Doctors call the latter *retrograde ejaculation.*

It is always worthwhile to ask the treating physician whether there are any alternative drugs available. Within the medical profession it is still a point of discussion whether patients should be warned about possible unfavourable side-effects before they start taking the medication, particularly when they concern a person's sexuality. In general, it is advisable to talk about possible sexological changes before starting treatment. In this way, the patient becomes aware that the doctor is willing to talk to him about this subject. In addition, it can also be established whether the patient has any existing problems in this area. If at a later date it is necessary to find out whether there is a possible relationship between sexual problems and the medication, this data can be very useful.

On the other hand, it is not unreasonable to wonder whether mentioning possible erectile problems with the use of a certain medication for high blood pressure, might turn into a self-fulfilling prophecy. Fortunately, many patients these days read the information slips supplied with the medication and then come forward themselves with questions about possible side-effects. If this happens, the doctor will convey that these side-effects are fairly uncommon and that it cannot be predicted who will have them and who will not. As mentioned above, it is wise to talk about possible side-effects. By using this approach the patients will be reassured and more willing to come forward about their sexual problems.

Nevertheless it is not unusual for patients to make an association between their sexual problems and the medication they are taking, but not dare to talk about it. It might even happen that they stop taking the medication without telling their doctor. As such a patient's blood pressure will not decrease sufficiently, he will be given a higher dose of the medication or more medication, which he will not take either. When the patient comes for a check-up, the doctor can ask him whether he is suffering from any side-effects in a sexual field and this can open the way to talking about it. This will undoubtedly increase so-called therapy compliance.

Alcohol and drugs
Quite a lot of men believe that regularly drinking alcoholic beverages increases their potency. They are totally mistaken. Chronic excessive use of alcohol usually leads to impotence. In time, alcohol affects the central and peripheral nervous system. Alcohol also has a toxic effect on the function of the testicles. Less testosterone is produced and the

liver gradually loses its capacity to break down oestrogen (men also produce small quantities of this female hormone). Symptoms associated with these phenomena are withering of the testicles and breast development.

In contrast with men, sexual arousal in women increases under the influence of alcohol. Why does this happen? This question intrigued the Finnish researchers Erikson and Lindman and their Japanese colleague Fukunaga. In the summer of 1994, they published their findings in the prestigious journal *Nature*. In both sexes, sexual interest and sexual arousal are related to the amount of testosterone in the blood. In women, the production of this 'male' sex hormone (by the adrenal glands) varies with the menstrual cycle: the testosterone level is highest in the fertile period around ovulation. The researchers found that a relatively small amount of alcohol (two glasses of beer or wine) was sufficient to increase a woman's testosterone level. The effect was only observed during ovulation in women who were not on the pill. In pill users who stopped taking the pill, the effect was even stronger, because the contraceptive pill keeps the testosterone level fairly low during the whole menstrual cycle.

In the previous century, the effect of various sorts of wine was a serious subject of study. Vecki believed that the heavier, darker red wines, such as Bordeaux, Dalmatian, Californian and some Spanish wines, could all have a positive influence on potency. Champagne, in contrast, was crippling. It might increase a man's libido, but 'his erectile equipment is sorely affected'.

In relation to the influence of alcohol on potency, William Shakespeare (1564-1616) gives a fitting description in Macbeth: 'It provokes the desire, but it takes away the performance'. The wise lesson that can be learnt from this is that the erectile mechanism does not approve of excessive alcohol use. It is sometimes said that impotence is a question of wanting to, but not being able to. In relation to excessive alcohol use, the opposite is usually valid: being able to, but not wanting to.

An interesting story about alcohol abuse and impotence can be found in *Hoffman's Honger* (*Hoffman's Hunger*) by Leon de Winter. He describes how the ambassadors Felix Hoffman and Jef Voeten in Nairobi, blind drunk, wish to satisfy their sensual lusts. Their wives have stayed at home. Outside the hotel, a line of prostitutes are waiting. In vulgar language, the two cast doubt of each other's potency:

> *'But you are drunk, Jef, you won't be able to get it up'.*
> *'I'll get it up!! I will! But you won't, Felix, I don't reckon you've been able to get it up for ages'.*
> *'Then I'll have to disappoint you, dear boy, because I am an expert in the sack.'*

They decide to take one of the prostitutes with them and climb into a taxi. The agreed price is fifty dollars, thirty for the service and twenty to rent her shabby hut. Hoffman had to prove himself in front of his drunken colleague. He could not manage and both gentlemen tried to escape without paying. They did not manage that either. One of them became injured and an oil lamp was knocked over. The hut caught fire and burned to the ground. Early the next morning ambassador Hoffman was arrested. The local authorities made it clear to him that money can do a lot of good under such circumstances. The commissioner received one thousand dollars, two inspectors received one hundred each, sixteen constables received ten dollars each and the destitute woman received three thousand dollars to build a new hut, even though it would not cost more than a couple of hundred.

Nicotine reduces potency because of its vasoconstrictive effect. The penis simply has less blood circulating through it. This has been proved by research into dogs that breathed in a fixed amount of nicotine.

The influence of 'recreational drugs' depends on the way in which they are used (smoking, sniffing, intravenous) and how much is taken. In addition, it is not unusual for several drugs to be used simultaneously.

Marihuana, methadon and heroin not only lower the testosterone level in the blood, but also increase the prolactin level. Too much of the latter hormone (that stimulates milk production in lactating women) leads to a sharp decrease in sexual desire.

A very high prolactin level in the blood is sometimes caused by a 'prolactinoma', which is a tumour of the pituitary gland. Depending on its size, the solution must be sought in medicinal treatment, radiotherapy or (micro)surgery.

Congenital abnormalities

Several years ago, the Dutch Society of Urologists addressed the question of whether an adult man can function satisfactorily if he is born with a severe abnormality of his external genitals. In a small-scale study on adult men who had been born with an 'open' bladder and in association with this had a severely deformed short penis, researchers found that seven out of the eleven men were satisfied about their sexual functioning. Four apparently were not. Very few studies of this sort have been published in the scientific literature.

In his posthumously published diary *The Business of Living*, the Italian author Cesare Pavese (1908-1950) describes his life as a lost battle. Pavese was impotent on the basis of a congenital abnormality of his genital organ. He recounts a fight with his own character, which over the years, he considers to be more and more of an unavoidable destiny. When Pavese committed suicide in 1950, he accomplished something that he had been looking forward to for a long time. A great deal was written and speculated about his reasons for committing suicide: criticism and a lack of understanding in left-wing circles, the fact that no woman had dared to bind herself to him, but chiefly also his impotence.

Several fragments from his diary:

7 December 1937

If it were true that man has freedom of choice, would he talk so much about it? Who can say this is not merely an assumption? In some things one can be free, if one so wishes; in others, one is bound

by the effects of previous action. But the initial choice?
A man who has not come up against a barrier of some physical impossibility that affects his whole life (impotence, dyspepsia, asthma, imprisonment, etc.) does not know what suffering is. In fact, such causes bring him to a decision of renouncement: a despairing attempt to make a virtue out of what is, in any case, inevitable. Could anything be more contemptible?

23 December 1937

The child who passes his days and nights among men and women, knowing vaguely but not believing that this is reality, troubled, in short, that sex should exist at all, does he not foreshadow the man who spends his time among men and women, knowing, believing that this is the only reality, suffering atrociously from his own mutilation? This feeling that my heart is being torn out and plunged into the depths, this giddiness that rends my breast and shatters me, is something I did not experience even when I was befooled in April.

The fate reserved for me (like the rat, my boy!) was to let the scar heal over, and then (with breath, a caress, a sigh) to have it torn open again and a new infection added.

Neither deception nor jealousy have ever given me the vertigo of the blood. It took impotence, the conviction that no woman ever finds pleasure with me, or ever would. We are as we are; hence this anguish. If nothing else, I can suffer without feeling ashamed: my pangs are no longer those of love. But this, in very truth, is pain that destroys all energy: if one is not really a man, if one must mix with women without being able to think of possessing them, how can one sustain one's spirits and vital power? Could a suicide be better justified?

With love or with hate, but always with violence.

Going to prison is nothing: coming back from it is frightful.

The average man ought to be well disciplined, not a street-loafer. I am neither the one nor the other.

There is something sadder than growing old - remaining a child.

25 December 1937
If screwing was not the most important thing in life, Genesis would
not have started with it.
   Naturally, everybody says to you 'What does it matter? That's
not the only thing. Life is full of variety. A man can be good for
something else,', but no one, not even the men will look at you
unless you radiate power. And the women will say to you: 'What
does it matter,' and so on, but they marry someone else. And to
marry means building a whole life, a thing you will never do. Which
shows you have remained a child too long.

Paraplegia

Paraplegia is a disaster. For this group of often young patients, there
are countless therapies available. They can have physiotherapy, water
therapy, occupational therapy, psychotherapy, you name it. However,
sex therapy is missing. Not only professional care providers, but also
family members believe that nothing more will ever become of sex.
They wonder in all seriousness whether and to what extent a person
can love an injured body.

   The author D.H. Lawrence (1885-1930) writes about this theme in
his, at that time, shocking novel *Lady Chatterly's Lover*, which now
finds itself on the book list at secondary schools. Lawrence describes
the ups and downs of husband and wife Chatterly; husband Chatterly
is a war invalid. He became a complete paraplegic at the age of twenty-
nine. Lady Chatterly was twenty-three years old at that time. Before
the accident, her husband Clifford had already proved to be a cold fish.
With his great penmanship, Lawrence describes Lady Chatterly's
passionate affair. First with a certain Michaelis, but his pathetic
'spasms of two seconds' ultimately do not satisfy her. Later she has
an affair with Mellors, the gamekeeper, the personification of the
natural male element, as a complete contrast with her wheelchair-
ridden, impotent husband.

   Particularly in the early stages of the handicap, the paraplegic often sees his sex life as a thing of the past. In a later stage, spasticity or frozen joints can stand in the way of sexual activities. In addition, urinary incontinence may be an added problem.

A positive aspect is that new erogenous zones can develop, such as the nipples, the neck, the lobes of the ears or the skin at the transition zone between the numb part of the body and the sensitive part. The sexual needs of these patients without a partner are especially high. For this reason, among others, there is an organisation of volunteers in Holland who travel the country to provide sexual services to the handicapped.

When a handicapped person does have a partner and that person provides most of the care, this sometimes suppresses the feeling of being each other's lover. Irritations between a healthy partner and a handicapped one are usually associated with the provision of care. In the words of a paraplegic: 'If you have just had a row with your wife and half an hour later you have to ask her to help put you on the toilet, then that's not funny at all', . Experts advise that the greater part of the care required by a severely handicapped person should not be provided by the partner, but by a professional. In this way it can perhaps be prevented that within the relationship, nursing wins hands down from loving.

If the healthy person wishes to end the relationship with his/her handicapped partner, feelings of guilt can lead to postponement of the decision. Feelings of responsibility and concern about what will happen and whether the handicapped partner will be able to manage, play a role. It is important to make a distinction between love and feeling sorry for a person. According to some psychologists, it is not a good idea to stay with someone out of sympathy. Others believe that love can change into 'sharing the suffering': the feeling that you share and feel the suffering of the other person. This does not detract from it being a very difficult decision to end a relationship, particularly if friends and relatives take the side of the one who is left behind. Lady Chatterly stayed, but chose an alternative solution - perhaps not such a bad one.

Wedding night impotence

One day I received a telephone call from a psychologist who asked whether I would teach a patient to give himself injections into his penis. What was the problem? A twenty-five year old Turkish man would shortly be returning to his fatherland to collect his wife. They had only been married for a few weeks, when his in-laws came to take her home again because the poor groom had not been able to get an erection on their wedding night. His wife had remained a virgin, a disgrace to her family. Under the motto 'now or never', I taught the man how to give himself injections. If he did not get an erection spontaneously, then he would have to resort to an injection in the penis. He departed with needles, syringes and several ampules of papaverine, a vaso-dilator, which will cause an erection when injected into the penis. A number of weeks later, we heard that he had managed without an injection and that he had been able to show the blooded sheet to his in-laws.

Psychologically most correctly, the famous French author Guy de Maupassant (1850-1893) described an unsuccessful wedding night in his story *Roger's Method*. In the evening after their wedding, a couple arrived in Paris, full of passion and desire. They withdrew to the bridal suite of the hotel. But the new husband, called Roger, was utterly incapable of getting an erection.

She did what she could, and for my part I made heroic attempts - it wouldn't work. Then she started to tease me - that's just the way she is - I can't say that she became ironic, but in my condition I certainly felt very suspicious.

'Can't you manage, can't you manage?', she smiled derisively. 'Can you after all?'

I became very angry. 'Shut up!', I shouted. 'Stop teasing me like that!'

'Who is teasing who?', she giggled. 'If you had any idea about my expectations this first time. You looked like such a fiery lover!'

I wanted to cry with shame and fury. I saw myself lying there

through her eyes: a worthless lump.
And she just lay there saying 'Come on! Gee up! Action!', while she
was almost choking with giggles.

Fury and shame drove the new husband on to the street. In desperation, he wanted to prove himself immediately. He followed a prostitute to her room and without any problem, managed to do with her what he had been unable to do half an hour earlier. With a feeling of recovered self-esteem, he returned to the hotel and demonstrated the secrets of love to his wife, this time with a stiff penis.

Undoubtedly, wedding night impotence also occurs in Holland, but for other reasons. On the big day the groom might have had too much to drink, or more commonly, is too tired.

Adultery

With his statement 'you can better get married than burn in hell' almost two thousand years ago, apostle Paul unwillingly agreed that human sexuality must have an escape valve one way or another. As a result, marriage - the institution within which sexuality can be indulged - became accepted by the church. But it was not blessed, that came later. Apostle Paul's attitude had far-reaching consequences for western civilisation. For a very long time, marriage was indissoluble. It is only fairly recently that divorce has become possible.

People not only seek sexual satisfaction within their marriage or relationship, but also outside and they will keep on doing so until the end of time. Extra-relational or extramarital sex holds great attraction, even for people who do not actually do it in practice. In fantasy, many people commit adultery. The research project *Sexuality in the Netherlands* by Van Zessen and Sandfort showed that 60% of the women and 80% of the men fantasized about having sex with someone other than their own partner. Figures on actual adultery vary so widely that it is impossible to say anything convincing about it. It probably happens more often than we think.

We are left with the problem that impotence is not uncommon

during extra-relational or extra-marital sex. You have been warned! The man might be feeling guilty that he is cheating on his partner. With his unfaithfulness, the man will cause his partner a great deal of grief and painful humiliation.

A case in point is a poem by Goethe, in which he describes how he meets a pretty young woman at a country inn. The attraction is mutual and they soon end up in bed together. However, at the crucial moment, his penis lets him down. He expresses the associated feelings of fury and shame in his poem 'Das Tagebuch': 'He who is otherwise so ruttish the Lord of Love, gives way like an inexperienced youth'. Anxiety and despair strike home, destiny becomes fate. The author of the poem wishes to be 'there where it rains halberds, rather than here the subject of insult and ridicule'.

In his desperation he shouts: 'My sole is full with thousands of curses'. The first-person narrator cannot get over the fact that he is unable to give a better performance. Despite the failure, his bed-mate appears satisfied. After all, she has experienced his love and tenderness. Freely translated:

She seems comforted by a loving word, a kiss, as though that was all her heart desired. How chaste she flatters herself with her beautifully curved form, filled with joy at my side, and she rests with me with an unfulfilled desire.

In the seventeenth verse, salient details come to light. The first-person narrator switches rather abruptly from his amorous adventure at the inn to his official marriage ceremony with his lawful wife. During the church ceremony, his 'iste' (Goethian for penis) cannot behave itself. Freely translated, the last few lines of the verse are: 'How strength grows into lust between the young couple, and when I was eventually allowed to lead her to the altar, I have to admit, my penis came back to life in the sight of Jesus our Saviour. Let God forgive me!'

The actual moral of Goethe's diary is that impotence is God's punishment for adultery. Isn't the sacrament of marriage aimed at avoiding impurity and at achieving procreation of the species in an orderly manner? Who can describe the surprise about an article in a Dutch national newspaper on 18 April 1995 under the heading: 'Bishop: adultery is in the genes'. In the article Richard Holloway, Anglican bishop of Edinburgh, asserts that the church should not condemn adultery. 'You can't blame people for committing adultery. That is the way God made them. It's in their genes.' He came to this conclusion in response to a series of lectures in which he tried to lift the taboo on sex. 'I am not a supporter of polygamy, but our instincts are polygamous. The sooner we realise this, the sooner we will be able to curb our desires. If we give them the free hand, this will cause our partner a great deal of grief'. Despite the excuse of the genes, the reaction from the head of the Anglican church was clear: 'Adultery is and remains a sin'.

The courageous bishop was probably right. Monogamy is certainly not an inborn characteristic in humans. The large majority of cultures charted by anthropologists are polygamous. The socio-biologists believe that men have a deep-rooted urge to deposit their sperm by as many women as possible, in the same way that women want as many suppliers as possible to optimise their chance of pregnancy. This might explain why so many men and women have such difficulties: the spirit is willing, but the flesh is weak. This certainly does not only apply to our Judeo-Christian-rooted culture. Who did not feel Othello's real jealousy? He loves Desdemona. His jealousy mixes with the rage of an insulted man. In response to the question from the jealous spouse - Othello: 'What are you thinking about, what are you feeling?' - there is only the sickly answer of masochism, self-torture. The only solution for the other person's adultery is love itself: surrender, accepting the freedom of the beloved person. Impossible? Perhaps, but it is the only way out if we are trapped by jealousy. Love only survives by the grace of freedom. According to the Mexican Nobel prize winner Octavio Paz †, this freedom of love is a huge mystery, a paradox that grows in a psychological substratum, which unfortunately also contains poisonous plants, such as unfaithfulness, betrayal, jealousy and silence.

An unsatisfying partner

Some men cannot find real satisfaction with their own wife, whereas they do not have any trouble finding it with other women. The impotence is partner-related. There can be many reasons for this.

Bernhard Premsela (1890-1944) was a general practitioner in Amsterdam for twenty-six years. In addition, he was medical director of an institute for sexological therapy for many years. During his carrier, he had heard every possible question about sex and had learnt to answer them. These included questions about partner-related impotence.

He was of great service to many by writing his experience down in a book that was published under the title *Sexuologie in de Praktijk* (*Sexology in Practice*) in 1940. Premsela is famous for being one of the pioneers of Dutch sexology. However, in the chapter on the psychological causes of male 'relative impotence', the woman is severely reprimanded:

A neglected appearance is usually to blame. Some women think that when they get married, it is no longer necessary to pay careful attention to their dress and appearance. They look sloppy; an uncared for face and hands do the rest. But please do not misunderstand me: I am not an advocate of rouge, lipstick and plucked eyebrows. I detest this make-up, with which the average woman becomes lost in the herd, while her face loses every personal cachet that was what made up her charm.
I just mean the pleasant care which keeps a marriage fresh and interesting. A woman who neglects to do this, or does not know this, may have to pay dearly for her error, with relative impotence of her husband.

For many partners, a breath that smells of alcohol is an insurmountable objection against getting an erection. In my opinion, this factor occurs far more often than you would think.

Tobacco smells from the mouth or on the fingers are for some a powerful anti-feticistic factor, although I have also experienced that the smell of a cigar, pipe and even cigarettes, might be highly appreciated.

And about excess hair growth:

There are women, who already during their youth, have a different hair pattern than average. Two aspects can have an inhibiting effect on the libido of the man. Firstly, body hair. The average woman only has axillary hair and pubic hair. The latter, as secondary sex characteristic, have a horizontal line at the upper border. Many women deviate from the average and have more or less virile hair growth (not a horizontal upper border to their pubic hair, but a diamond shape that ends at the navel; hair on their breasts, arms and legs).

I have seen many cases in which impotence was the result of excessive hair growth on the upper legs, sternum and breasts.

A second aspect that can have a strong inhibitory effect on a man's feelings, is hair growth on the upper lip and chin. This can vary from very slight growth on the upper lip, which especially in dark women, can be very attractive to some men, to a moustache or beard. The latter can extinguish all sexual feelings. Therapy comprises removal, preferably as early as possible, of all hairs.

Naturally, Premsela was exaggerating, but there may be an element of truth in some of his assertions. At the same time it is also important to realise that for many women, sexual relations with their fat-bellied, beer-drinking husband is anything but a pleasant pastime!

In novel-writing, partner-related impotence is a popular subject. An example can be found in the *Afscheidswals* (*Goodbye Waltz*) by Milan Kundera. In the story, the trumpet player Bertlef describes his thoughts about this spiteful form of impotence:

'I am really deathly tired', he said.

She put her arms around him and led him to the bed: 'You'll see that I can soon make your tiredness disappear', she said and started to play with his naked body.

He lay there, as if he was lying on an operating table. He knew that every effort on his wife's part would be fruitless. His body withdrew into itself, disappeared inside, there was not a grain of expansion power in it. Kamila slid all over his body with her moist lips and he knew that she wanted to torture him and herself; he hated her [...].

She put her mouth on his stomach and felt how his genitals withered at her touch, how they fled from her, how they became smaller and smaller and more and more frightened. And he knew that Kamila read the lack of response from his body as a consuming love for another woman. He knew that she was tormenting herself; and the more she tormented herself, the more she tormented him by touching his impotent body with her moist lips.

Occupational impotence

Some men are in love with their work. They put all of their energy into it. This can lead to problems. The sexologist Bühl (1921) describes one of them in his book *Eros met Grijzende Slapen* (*Eros with Greying Temples*), namely 'occupational impotence'. Bühl also calls it 'scholar's impotence'. But any professor who might feel that this applies to him, does have consolation. He is in good company. King Louis XIV of France, Emperor Napoleon I, the composer Ludwig van Beethoven and the authors Gustave Flaubert, John Ruskin and Bernard Shaw were all renowned for their undersized sexual prowess. Impotence among famous mathematicians and physicists is a well-known phenomenon. It is said of Sir Isaac Newton that he never had coitus in his life.

Giving work one's full attention can destroy erotic interest. In reality it is more a case of not wanting to than not being able to. This voluntary impotence is no problem at all for the workaholics. They are not missing anything. However, conflicts can arise, because their partner is feeling (sexually) neglected.

Bühl amplifies this with the example of Heinrich E., an almost fifty-year-old engineer. He has been married for twelve years to a woman who is about ten years younger. A serious marriage crisis incites him to seek help. He said:

> *It is possible that she sometimes finds me strange when I am so absorbed in my work, but I always thought that she had got used to it. Naturally she feels that she is being shut out one way or another, but she does not understand anything about technical matters.*

The crisis was evoked by a forty-year-old journalist who Heinrich had met through his work. Afterwards he had invited him home because 'his wife also liked to see other people around her than his colleagues who were always going on about their work'.

> *He talked easily, while I hardly spoke at all. I believe that my wife realised that there was not very much behind all that talk - but, anyhow, he was offering her something that I never gave her. I knew that nothing had happened yet, as people say. When I asked my wife what she thought of the man, she answered that I had obviously forgotten that I was a man and she was a woman. And she was right.*

Next, the unfortunate engineer describes how he tries to satisfy his wife sexually, but fails miserably. The therapist explains that it is not so much the long period of abstinence, as the sudden compulsion behind exercising his will that is the problem:

> *You were standing, shall we say, with one leg still in your work. But you should forget that just as quickly as this crisis. In precisely the same way as you dedicate yourself to your work to make it a success, you must give yourself totally to love. A long holiday with*

your wife, that is the best thing. Far away from everything, you will
best be able to turn back to what you have forgotten.

A very few men use sex to charge their batteries as it were. No
matter how tired they are feeling, it is always convenient for them to
have sex. A famous example of this was John F. Kennedy. This does
not apply to the majority of us.

Wandering thoughts

How long is your record for maintaining an erection? This was the
question that a few thousand American students were asked in the
study by Kinsey. What did they find? In 4% it was less than five
minutes, in 18% it was six minutes to a quarter of an hour, in 19% it
was a quarter of an hour to a half hour, in 26% it was a half hour to an
hour, in 15% it was one or two hours, in 5% it was two to three hours
and in 4% it was three hours or longer. Older readers will undoubtedly
have to think very deeply, because such records are established in a
man's youth.

Some men lose their erection prematurely because they
unconsciously take the 'spectator's' role. Their thoughts start to
wander. They are no longer taking part in the proceedings. Their
erection wilts.

Rousseau (1712-1778) describes his experience of this in his book
Bekentenissen (Confessions). The story is about an ill-fated adventure
with the Venetian courtesan Giulietta. Full of passion, he appears at
her bedside. He hardly has time to admire her in all her beauty, before
he has a thought that brings him to tears and completely distracts him
from his original intentions. He continues to work on this thought and
his feelings of desire evaporate.

Instead of the flames that were engulfing me, I suddenly felt an icy
chill running through my veins, my legs trembled and while I was
nearly fainting, I sat down and cried like a child.
Who could guess the cause of my tears, who could guess what was

going through my head at that moment? I said to myself: what I have here is a perfect creation of nature and love. The spirit, the body, everything is perfect. She is just as good and noble as she is beautiful and captivating. The giants of the earth, the kings, should be her slaves. Sceptres should be lying at her feet.

The adventure ends in a humiliating fiasco, because the young Jean-Jacques suddenly notices that the courtesan has only one nipple. He blames his impotence - what else would you expect - on the courtesan:

I lost my head, looked harder and realised that one breast was not formed like the other. Then I started to wonder how anyone could have a breast without a nipple and, convinced that it must be like that because of some serious inborn defect, I saw, after having weighed the thought thoroughly, as clear as crystal that the most charming woman I could ever imagine, was no more than a sort of monster, the refuse of nature, people and love. In my bluntness I went so far as to start speaking about the missing nipple. At first she viewed the matter from the sunny side and in an elated mood she said and did things that should have been enough to make me die of love. But because I could not shake my feelings of uneasiness, which I was unable to hide from her, she finally started to blush; she pulled her clothes back into place, straightened up and without a word went to sit by the window.

The scene ends with the proverbial exclamation from the disappointed and angry courtesan: 'Lascia le donne, e studia la matematica.' (Leave women alone, and stick to the study of mathematics).

Penile injuries

Impotence can also be caused by injury to the penis or testicles. A sudden movement during coitus or masturbation can sometimes tear the wall of one of the cavernous bodies. The coital position in which the woman rides the man with her back to him is not without risk. The penis can be more or less bent double against the woman's pubic bone. Tearing is usually accompanied by a snapping sound, which is why urologists call the injury a penis fracture. An operation to stitch the tear is the only remedy.

If a woman is being threatened by rape, the best thing she can do is try to fracture the man's penis with her hand. Another option is for the woman to contract her pelvic floor muscles as tightly as possible so that the man breaks his penis when he tries to enter her by force. If she is successful, the rapist must seek immediate medical attention from a urologist, because repair at a later stage is almost impossible and the man runs a considerable risk of remaining impotent. It is therefore logical that if a man comes in for treatment because he has a penis fracture, a sexologically-oriented urologist will always consider the possibility of a sexual crime or very rough sex.

The urological literature often contains reports about bite wounds to the penis. Apparently, oral-genital sex has not yet lost its popularity. Such bite wounds are often complicated by bacterial infection and there is also the risk of transmitting hepatitis or HIV.

A nasty consequence of oral-genital sex is described in John Irving's novel *The World According to Garp*, which is about the life of a young American author in the nineteen sixties. Out of revenge for his infidelity, Garp's wife Helen has started a relationship with one of her students. While Garp is at the cinema with the children, Helen and her lover Michael Milton are sitting in his car which is parked in the driveway of the Garp residence. Helen tries to convince him of her intention to end their relationship. In the end Michael promises to disappear from her life for good on the condition that she will satisfy him just once with oral sex - in the car because they had often fantasized about doing it there:

His hand flew to Helen's throat and gripped her hard; with his other hand he undid his flies.
'Michael!', she protested sharply.

'You always said that you wanted to', he reminded her.[....]
'But it was much too dangerous, you said. It's not dangerous now.
The car is parked. We won't have an accident like this.'

Michael Milton then displays his most vulgar side - and that is just what Helen needs at that moment. She realises that after ejaculating, a man usually quickly loses interest. And her experiences in Michael's flat had taught her that it would not take long with him either. Time was also playing a major role. If Garp and the children had gone to the shortest possible film, she would only have twenty minutes left. So she begins with great determination, as if it is the last stage of an unpleasant task.

Earlier than expected, Garp and the children return home from the cinema. Apparently they had not enjoyed the film. As was his habit, Garp drove the last bit of the journey without lights and with the motor switched off. He turned into the driveway, but there was a car parked in it...

Helen's head was jerked forward and just missed the steering wheel, but it hit her in the neck.[...] Helen's mouth slammed shut with such force that she broke two teeth and had to have two careful stitches in her tongue.

At first she thought that she had bitten off her tongue, because she could feel it lying loose in her mouth which was full of blood; but her head hurt so much that she did not dare to open her mouth until she reallyhad to breathe - and in addition she found that could not move her right arm. She spat what she thought was her tongue into the palm of her left hand. Obviously, it was not her tongue. It was about three quarters of Michael Milton's penis.
Garp broke his jaw during the collision and could not speak for a long time. In a note to his wife he wrote: 'Three quarters is not enough!'

Fortunately, injury to the penis usually leads to only temporary impotence. An interesting example is described in *Turks Fruit* (*Turkish Fruit*) by Jan Wolkers. The male central figure had thumbed a lift from the red-haired Olga and had just made passionate love to her during a short break:

> *And I was still thinking that she was so wonderful, that when I did up the zip of my trousers, I forgot that I hadn't put my prick back into my underwear. I screamed with pain and could not move.*
>
> *The skin of my dick was caught between the copper teeth. At first we laughed about it, because I thought that I would be able to get it out, just like I used to do with the flakes of skin from my neck when I did up the zip of my jumper.*

At a surgical outpatient clinic, the zip problem is usually solved by using a scalpel to removing the piece of foreskin caught in the zip. This has proved to be the least painful solution.

The zip has a double symbolic meaning, which can be summarized by two adjectives: 'mechanical' and 'sexual'. The combination provides the key: mechanical sexuality, but also injured sexuality. In this way the zip is an instrument of seduction and an instrument that, whether or not in erection, can damage the penis.

At the beginning of the nineteen seventies, a series of penis amputations were reported in Thailand. More than one hundred abused women believed that they could solve their problems in this fashion. Usually the penis was thrown out of the window, so that the ducks could eat it (the houses were built on top of poles and the people kept ducks underneath). Surgical reconstruction was only possible in eight men.

At the end of 1993, the whole of America fell under the spell of the 'penis law suit'. Lorena Bobbitt, a twenty-three-year-old manicurist, was brought to trial for cutting off her husband's penis. Often in a state of drunkenness, he had raped her time and time again, until she decided that it was the limit.

The law suit became a parade of experts, doctors, psychologists and criminologists. They talked for hours about the meaning of the penis as a symbol of power. The trial was regarded to be 'a fight between the sexes' by a number of feminist groups. Although they did not try to justify her deed, they did maintain that if she was convicted, it would mean a slap in the face for all women who had ever been abused. Fortunately, Lorena did not have to go to prison. The feminists' voice had obviously been heard when they threatened to castrate one hundred Americans if she was put behind bars!

Nine months later - what do you think of the timing! - the video *John Wayne Bobbitt Uncut* was released. During the promotion campaign the ex-nightclub owner made no secret of the fact that he had found it terrific to make a porno film in which he played the leading role. In answer to the question of whether it was going too far to demonstrate that his penis was still functioning normally by means of a porno film, he said that 'everyone was intrigued after all, and in this way I can convince everyone that *he* is still working perfectly, despite the fact that coitus is a bit painful now and then.'

After Lorena's trial, it became rather popular to take revenge on one's partner by cutting off his penis. On average, about one penis a fortnight is cut off somewhere in the world.

In the literature I found a similar story to that of Lorena. In his book *Something Quite Different*, Guiseppe Culichia describes what a woman is capable of if she is treated with indifference by her husband. The woman is deeply unhappy. She cannot believe that she was ever in love with her husband. Shouting and getting drunk, those are the only things he can do. In addition, he is morbidly jealous of his wife, whose career is going so well. One day the wife - by coincidence - walks into a hardware shop and sees an electric saw. On impulse she asks the assistant if the saw is really sharp. When he confirms this, she decides to buy the saw. At the time she was not sure what she was going to do with it.

Some while later, her husband comes home drunk and after a shouting match, followed by rape, he falls asleep. Then she decides to use the saw:

She unrolled the long black flex and pushed the plug into the socket where the television had been. Then, very slowly, she peeled back the bedclothes. As usual, Guido was sleeping peacefully. He always slept deeply. He had hairy legs. Barbara pressed the red button. The boy at the shop was right. The electric saw sawed with all its might.

War and torture

In Biblical, *Deuteronomy* chapter 23, Moses wrote 'He that is wounded in the stones, or hath his privy member cut off shall not be permitted to enter into the congregation of the Lord'. As an innocent youngster I found this a fairly heavy pronouncement, which I did not understand until I read the book by Dufour: *The History of Sexual Customs of all Races and all Times*. What was the case in Moses' day? When Jewish men fought among themselves, they were in the habit of grabbing their opponents genitals in order to win. Even their wives sometimes made themselves useful. Under the title: 'Against shamelessness' in *Deuteronomy* it says: When men fight among each other and the wife of one of them comes between them to free him from the hands of the one who is beating him and she puts out her hand and grips his genitals, then she will have her hand cut off; she shall not be spared. Things were quite different in Lorena Bobbitt's case! To put an end to these practises, Moses made the law that a castrated man or one whose penis had been amputated could no longer attend Yahweh's gathering.

Bullet and shrapnel injuries are more in keeping with modern times. In the Vietnam war, in South Africa before Mandela and in Bosnia-Hercegovina these injuries have been described extensively. However, it is not only in times of war that the penis suffers gunshot wounds. Some while ago, a fifteen-year-old boy was admitted to hospital because a pimp had shot him in the genitals with a shotgun. How had that happened? Together with a few of his friends, he had started up a conversation with a window prostitute. Not only in her opinion, but also in that of her pimp, the conversation had taken too long. They had not been able to reach an agreement. The youngsters were therefore advised to leave. Unfortunately, they did not heed the advice. The lead shot had dramatic effects: one of the eight pellets that had met their target lodged in the middle of the right cavernous body of the boy's penis. Under general anaesthetic, the penis was circumcised and the skin was stripped off (just like preparing a smoked eel). After a long search, the pellet was found and removed. Fortunately, the urethra was not damaged and the penis appeared to function as of old.

During the war at the beginning of this century, the Arabs had the nasty habit of mutilating Turkish soldiers that had been shot dead. They amputated the penis and put it in the victim's mouth. The reason for doing this was that they believed that when the soldier eventually entered heaven, he would certainly not be able to enjoy sexual relations. The same sort of thing happened in former Yugoslavia. According to some stories, soldiers that were taken prisoner had to eat the penises of their deceased comrades in arms.

The ancient Egyptians did not flinch either. In about 1300 B.C., the Egyptian general Meneptah returned from battle in what is now known as Lebanon. As spoils of war he brought 1235 amputated penises! A written memory of this can be found on a monument in Karnak in Egypt. In *Samuel* 18 it is described how Saul sent his future son-in-law, David, to obtain his bride's price: one hundred foreskins of Philistines. It was Saul's intention that David would fall in battle. However, David managed to collect two hundred foreskins. Consequently, Saul agreed that his daughter Michal would marry David.

There are also descriptions of women torturing men. The sexologist Havelock Ellis, who believes that the penis is more sensitive than the vagina, described a man who consulted him with a swollen, itching penis:

The night before, just before coitus, the woman had injected carbolic acid into her vagina. The man, unaware, felt unpleasant

burning and pain during and after coitus, but did not think any more
about it and fell asleep. The next morning he had large blisters on
his penis, but it was no longer painful.

The man's foreskin was rolled back and swollen, his whole penis
was puffy and there were large, raw sores on both sides of his glans.

Perverted thoughts

It is impossible to write about impotence without addressing the
question of abnormal, deviant or perverse sexuality. The modern view
is that sexual conduct is not perverse as long as it is performed by adults
and does not cause physical or psychological damage to either of the
partners. Therefore it is very difficult to lay down standards about
what is normal and what is perverse. In his book *Het Jaar van de Kreeft*
(*Cancer Year*) Hugo Claus describes how a man cannot get an erection
when his girlfriend invites him to have anal sex with her.

'Oh dear', he said, 'I would really like another little sandwich like
the one this afternoon, at the side of the road.

She turned half onto her knees, stuck her buttocks in the air,
pulled them apart and wiggled them up and down. 'Do it here for
a change', she whispered. It was too difficult, he plunged too
urgently, too hastily. She put in some Nivea cream, but he
continued to thrust against the closed entry, surprised by the
sudden invitation and at the same time nervous about defloration
there. When she swore grumpily and disappointedly, he wilted
immediately.

'Then it has to be the usual hole', she said, and turned over.

Some men have strange ideas about the female sexual organ
(vagina). Not only that it is equipped with teeth, but also that a woman
has two vaginas instead of one. This is an old theme that is described
by the italian Giovanni Francesco Poggio in his fifteenth century Liber
Facetiarum: a complete idiot of a farmer, who knows nothing about
sex, gets married. In bed he thrusts his spear into his wife's behind.
Delighted with his successful attempt, he asks her whether she might

perhaps have two vaginas. One is enough for him, the second is unnecessary. His wife, who is having an affair with the parish priest, makes the suggestion of giving up her second vagina to the church. Her husband agrees. The farmer and his wife invite the priest to dinner. After the meal, all three of them get into bed together. The priest puts his penis in first and the idiot farmer is satisfied with his share. 'Remember our agreement, use your own share and leave mine to me', said the farmer. The priest answers 'As God is my witness, I do not desire your share, as long as I can use the share of the church'. The priest can continue to do as he wishes.

The story reminds me of the farmers from the province of Brabant who used to make a distinction in relation to their wives, between a week-day hole and a Sunday hole. Unfortunately I cannot remember which hole was reserved for the Holy day.

The famous Roman emperor Nero tended to boast about his work as a poet and was frequently encouraged by the whim of erotic frenzy. He often cloaked himself in animal skins, sometimes as a wolf, lion, swan or bull. He attacked chained prisoners and then scratched, bit or mutilated them for his own pleasure. From time to time he presented himself as a woman at orgies. The emperor died in tears in the arms of his wife Sporus. She had taken very great care that her blood had not mingled with that of her husband. His whole body was covered with stinking wounds, which were the result of his countless sexual encounters.

One thing is certain: sexual perversion chiefly occurs in men. People have suggested various reasons for this. Kinsey associated sexual perversion with the dependence on psychological stimulation and the tendency to fantasize about sex and about women in general. He also mentioned the fact that men in contrast with women 'are more easily governed by objects that are associated with these experiences'. Havelock Ellis tried to find an explanation by pointing out that exercising male power and dominance over women is a sign of primitive courtship.

Sexual perversion is difficult to describe, particularly as opinions change according to the time and location. President Clinton can tell you more about it!

Similar problems surround paedophilia. Not so long ago, the megastar Michael Jackson was accused of regularly having sex with young boys. In *De Gaykrant* (*Gay Newspaper*) published on 18 August 1995, there was a story about how a thirteen-year-old boy who claims to have been abused, drew a picture of the sexual organ of the famous pop star. According to the American Public Prosecutor, the drawing matched Jackson's penis. The Public Prosecutor was able to draw this conclusion because during an earlier investigation, photographs had been taken of the performer's penis. Jackson said that he was suffering from a pigmentation abnormality on his penis, which according to him, had left behind 'certain' characteristics. The Public Prosecutor remarked that the characteristics were strikingly well-reflected in the drawings. These then threw new light on the investigation into Jackson's alleged child abuse. Earlier, the superstar maintained that he had never taken photographs of naked young boys. However, a search of his house revealed a whole book full of nude photos.

In an ironic manner, Hans Plomp describes the amusing and just as strange adventures of a perverse art critic in his book *Het Innerlijk Bordeel* (*The Inner Brothel*). Although Plomp is not one of the most renowned writers, he is known among experts as the most pro-female Dutch author. And that is worth a great deal! In his book he describes how Barels becomes as good as impotent after having a frightening experience during coitus. Surreptitiously, the art critic turned the mirrors on his wife's dressing table in such a way that he could see himself in action during coitus. He hoped that as usual, his wife would fall asleep during the performance. Then he would have all the time in the world.

One evening, he is very insistent about having coitus with her, while she is not in the mood at all. Nevertheless she allows him to do as he pleases. As expected, she soon falls asleep. Actually he is very pleased about that, because he does not like her to lie staring at him while he is jostling about on top of her. She always looked so uninterested and contemptuous. Carefully he pulls the bedclothes back. The sleeping woman gave a quick snort on being disturbed, but she did not wake up. Barels looked into the mirror behind him. Only one lamp was burning on the night table, but he could clearly see his whiter-than-white buttocks reflected in the glass. He strained around a bit further to see better. Suddenly he stiffened. In the mirror he saw his wife's lower body and on top of her, not he, Barels, but a scabby white or greyish dog with bald patches on his back and behind. The beast grinned back at him in the mirror. Barels' breath caught in his throat and he lay dead still. Barels put his arm in the air. The beast raised its forepaw. He started to sweat profusely.

He reaches towards the light cord at the head of the bed and pulls it. In the light he can see the beast clearly. It looks like a scabby jackal. Barels groaned appalled and it sounded like a growl from a dog. His wife suddenly wakes up. 'Why are you lying there howling like a dog? Just leave me alone. I have a headache and you are all sticky with sweat'.

'Don't you notice anything strange about me?' asked Barels.

She stared at him once again with contempt. Then she said: 'You look just like a drowned dog. But that is nothing new.'

From that night onwards, Barels is as good as impotent. The few attempts that he makes are all pitiful failures. Moreover, Barels suggests a possible remedy for his impotence to his wife that he had read in the diary of James Joyce. The Irish master knew no greater pleasure than to lie under the buttocks of his wife so that she could defecate in his face. It was also Joyce who wrote: 'The smallest things give me a grandiose erection - a brown stain on the back of your knickers'. After Barels' suggestion, his wife left him.

Hans Plomp confirms that every man sometimes has strange, often perverse fantasies. But it is what he does with them or does not do with them that matters! Generally, it is not sensible to air such thoughts, unless you can earn money with them.

Solutions

Spanish fly, musk, garlic, grey amber (made from the rotting intestines of the sperm whale), vanilla, phosphorous, saffron, opium, chocolate, truffles, mushrooms, asparagus, vomit nuts, parsnips, ginger, cocoa, figs, calf's brains, crustaceans, salted meat, French beans, dried peas, red wine, beef marrow, fresh egg yolk, aromatic douches aimed at the 'offending part', cold enemas, all sorts of mineral water, acupuncture, electropuncture, galvanic (electric) power, electrical friction, cauterisation of the prostate, manure treatment, milk direct from a woman's breast. These are only a fraction of the kinds of remedies that have been described for impotence.

In Greek mythology, Aphrodite was the goddess of love and beauty. She was the daughter of Uranus, the personification of the heavens. The word aphrodisiac is derived from her name. Since the earliest historical writings, mankind has been preoccupied by aphrodisiacs. In every culture, people have been preparing love potions in the hope of recovering potency or increasing it in accordance with their wishes.

The oldest description of an aphrodisiac can be found in the Turkish and Islamitic Art Museum in Istanbul. It is written on a clay tablet from the thirteenth century B.C. in Hittitic cuneiform script. Freely translated it says the following:

If a man's potency comes to the end in the month Nisannu, you catch a male partridge, you pluck its wings, strangle it and flutter salt on it; you pound it up together with mountain Dadanu plant. You give it to him to drink in beer and then that man will get potency.

(...) if ditto: the penis of a male partridge, the saliva of a bull with an erection, the saliva of a goat with an erection. You give it to him to drink in water. Then wrap up in hair from the tail and wool from the perineum of a sheep and put it on his thigh and then he will get potency.

Reference is also made to an aphrodisiac in *Genesis* 30:14-17:

> *When Ruben went outside in the days of the wheat harvest, he found love apples in the fields, which he gave to his mother Leah. And Rachel said to Leah: Give me some of the love apples from your son. But she said to her: Is it not enough that you have taken my husband? And now you want to take the love apples from my son, too? Rachel said: That is why he will lie with you tonight, for the love apples from your son. When Jacob returned from the fields that evening, Leah went to meet him and said: Come to me, because I have hired you honestly for the love apples from my son. So he lay with her that night. And God heard Lea; she became pregnant and she bore Jacob a fifth son.*

Mandrake (the love apple) is also mentioned at another place in the *Old Testament*, in *Canticles* 7:13:

> *Mandrake gives its fragrance, and at our doors all sorts of precious fruits grow, young and old.*

The peasants found the mandrake during the harvest. It was very rare and in great demand, not only because of its delicious fragrance, but also because it could be used as a remedy for impotence and infertility. It contains a mucoid substance, sugar, resin, non-essential oils, tannin and various salts.

In southern Europe, it used to be common belief that mandrake chiefly grew at places where criminals had been hanged. According to legend, not only an erection but also ejaculation occurred during a man's death struggle on the gallows. The semen that had been entrusted to the earth under such exceptional circumstances was thought to generate fertile soil for the mandrake. The association between sexual arousal and strangulation or garrotting later became the subject of the books by the Marquis of Sade. And who has never heard of the term 'strangle sex'?

The old druids in Celtic cultures had great respect for mistletoe, a herb that was sacred in their eyes. They considered it to be a bad omen if mistletoe berries fell from the trees. They cut mistletoe for their new year ceremonies. That is probably the origin of hanging mistletoe in the home at Christmas. Mistletoe has also been used for medicinal purposes. Panoramix, the venerable druid from the village of Asterix and Obelix, cut mistletoe with his gold pruning knife to brew a magic potion that made his people invincible. 'But he also knows lots of other recipes...' as the writer put it, to phrase the thoughts of the adult comic reader.

With the Romans is was somewhat different. Besides the official physicians, there were also the so-called sagae. These were mostly greying prostitutes. They busied themselves on two fronts: as non-authorised midwives who induced abortions, or as concocters of love potions.

Just as nowadays, abortions were performed for various reasons: a prostitute would be hindered in the practice of her trade if she were pregnant, or a married woman might wish, for example, to destroy the evidence of an extramarital relationship. Julia, the daughter of Emperor Augustus, did not need abortions, because she only entertained lovers when she was pregnant by her spouse Agrippa. If people wondered how it was that all her children resembled her spouse despite her adulterous activities, then according to Macrobius she always said: 'I never take passengers aboard unless the ship is already fully loaded!'

Abortions gave the sagae plenty of work, but that only formed a small part of their industry. It was customary for these concocters of magic potions to visit the Esquiline hill at night. The hill was the stage for casting magic spells and making sacrifices. It was also the graveyard for slaves that had been buried here and there without even a shroud. It was not safe to go there at night. At the edge of the hill, close to the *Porta Metia*, stood the gallows and crosses, hung with the bodies of the condemned. The executioner's house naturally stood close by so that he could keep watch over his victims.

In these macabre surroundings, the sagae went about their work. By the light of the moon, they picked their magic herbs and plucked hair, bones and fat from the hanging corpses. According to Dufour, even children were sacrificed if an especially powerful potion was required. To perform such an awful deed, the sagae had to be paid a large sum of money, although the life of a child in Rome was not worth much. The child had to be stolen from its wet nurse or parents, buried alive and subsequently disembowelled, otherwise the liver, gall, prepuberal testicles and bone marrow would not have the real love-inciting power!

Some sagae were capable of making potions that could render a man completely impotent. This caused the Romans great anxiety. The official, respectable physicians thoroughly condemned the use of any sort of potion. Instead they recommended drinking natural mineral water containing sulphur and iron. However, it did need to be drunk close to the source. The further these *aquae amatrices*, as these tonics were called, were taken away from the source, the more they lost their power.

Musk has always been known as an aromatic love-inciting substance. It is secreted by the foreskin of the deer. The name is derived from the Sanskrit word for 'testicle', with the innuendo that the substance originates from a genital organ. Musk occurs fairly commonly in nature. It is secreted by the musk mole, the musk ox, the muscovy duck, the musk hyacinth, the musk cherry, musk wood, etc. and by many other animals and plants that bear the name musk. In the mating season, lizards and crocodiles secrete musk from the glands under their chin. Elephants do the same from their cheek glands.

Flower and plant fragrances can also have a positive influence on sexuality. Herb Robert (Geranium robertianum), St. John's Wort (Hypericum perforatum), the Barberry Flowers (Berberis vulgaris) and conkers from the horse chestnut all smell like semen. The same also applies to the crushed flowers of the henna plant (Lawsonis inurmis). Muslim women like to rub their palms with them. West European women dye their hair with henna. In the Far-East Ginseng (Panox quinquefolia) is frequently promoted as an aphrodisiac, but in fact it is a tonic. Herbalists say it should be considered as a compound that brings the body into balance. Ginseng has to be taken on a daily basis for several months before its benefits can be assessed.

The mustard plaster was invented by Hammond. The penis was coated with mustard and then wrapped in a circular bandage for several hours. According to this expert from the previous century, this form of treatment needed to be applied with caution. Otherwise inflammation could develop, or even cancer. In Hammond's own words: 'Generally, it is necessary to remove the plaster as soon as the patient starts to feel a burning sensation; at this point there is sufficient rash. It is not possible to say in advance how often the plaster can be reapplied. This depends on the result obtained and the level of stimulation achieved.'

Very occasionally, there is a scientific theory about the action of an alleged aphrodisiac. Boars (male pigs) with their churning and rooting spread the truffle over a large part of France. Truffles are a type of fungi (toadstool) that grow under the ground between the roots of the oak and hazel. They are considered a delicacy. Nowadays truffles are discovered by specially trained sows or bitches. Only they can smell where these fungi lie. The reason for this has something to do with alpha-androsterone - a hormone - which unjustly leads these female animals to believe that they are on the trail of a mate. In view of the fact that alpha-androsterone is also present in the axillary sweat of men and in the urine of women, it is possible that it incites unconscious sexual feelings. Better start eating truffles then!

The Chinese consider soup made from the nest of sea swallow to be the ultimate aphrodisiac. The nest is made of sea grass held together with roe. It is reputed to have rejuvenation properties. Sea grass contains a lot of the earlier-mentioned phosphorus.

The rare, almost extinct Japanese nut tree (Ginkgo biloba) is also well-known to the Chinese. An extract from the leaves can induce the smooth muscle cells of the cavernous bodies to relax and therefore cause an erection. In addition, the tree not only grows very tall, but can also reach an age of one thousand years. It has existed for 150 million years and has survived evolution largely unchanged - albeit with difficulty - since the Jurassic period. It is therefore not surprising that these trees have been planted in Buddhist temple gardens since time immemorial. Another scientific aspect of these trees is that swimming spermatozoa play a role in their reproduction. This is extremely rare in plants and trees. The fully developed seed has a fleshy yellow skin and smells like rancid butter. These seeds (nuts) are considered a delicacy in the Far East. Although considered safe for use by most people, Gingko biloba interferes with blood clotting, so it should not be taken by persons with clotting disorders.

Yohimbine (Pausinystalia yohimba) originates from Africa, the substance is derived from the bark of an evergreen. Taken by itself, yohimbine can produce erections, but unfortunately the occasional patient may experience excitational states such as nervousness, tremor, irritability, and insomnia as well as a diminished urge to urinate.

The persistent interest in all sorts of aphrodisiacs has meant that the Asian, Indian and Javanese rhinoceros are almost extinct. Even the African rhinoceros has become an endangered species. It is chiefly Eastern Asian and Middle Eastern people who believe that finely ground rhinoceros horn can improve potency. This is probably related to the fact that rhinoceros mate for about an hour at a time. Astronomical prices are paid for rhinoceros horn. In the autumn of 1995, the situation in Europe became so dreadful that Interpol recommended keeping an extra eye on rhinoceros at zoos. Poachers were even aiming at rhinoceros in captivity.

The Dutch do not have clean hands either in this respect. It is not so long ago that the iguana was threatened with extinction on the Dutch-Caribean island of Curaçao. Soup made from this beautiful reptile was believed to cure impotence. The genital organ of the iguana is shaped in such a way that it looks like he has two penises. Such an abnormal penile form has also been diagnosed in the human male. It concerned the twenty-two-year-old Portuguese gypsy Juan Baptista dos Santos. According to his doctors, he did indeed have two penises, both of which functioned normally; after he had ejaculated with one penis, he directly continued with the other. The patient preferred the left one, because it was thicker.

Not so long ago in Amsterdam, six policemen, an unpaid flora and fauna inspector and an inspector from the General Inspection Department went into action to confiscate three bottles of Chinese spirits from an off-licence. The reason for this show of strength? On his beat, an alert policeman had noticed bottles in the window of the off-licence that not only contained rice liquor, but also a lizard. The reptiles turned out to be geckos (Japaloua polygonata), a large Asian species of lizard. The liquor is called Ha Kai Chiew. The Chinese attribute healing properties to the juices from the fast and dexterous gecko, particularly for impotence. So-called conserving of animals is traditional in many countries. In France adders disappear into eau de vie, in Spain frogs and in Mexico worms.

In his book *Onder Professoren* (*Among Professors*) The Dutch author W.F.Hermans describes how professor Dingelam from Groningen wins the Nobel prize for inventing the 'whitener', a chemical compound that not only makes your washing whiter than white, but as it appeared later, can also restore male potency. The Japanese were responsible for discovering the latter application. Professor Gurrie emphasized to his colleague that administering whitener as a medication for impotence had enormous philosophical implications. Dingelam was to become the patron of elderly men. There was little respect for a man who was growing older, but that was about to change. If the potency of elderly men could be restored, then mankind would experience a revolutionary change. Gurrie predicted that a new man would arise through Dingelam's discovery:

So far doctors have only been able to increase the number of elderly people. That is something new, but not fundamentally new. Very elderly people, people who live for a very long time, they already existed before medical science meant anything. There weren't many of them, but whether there were many or few, doesn't make much difference in principle. It would be completely different if eighty-year-old men could still be potent. Because then their lives would become meaningful again. Then they will have lived for a long time, but they won't be really old...

Subsequently, the Nobel prize winner makes it clear that as far as he is concerned he can only wonder whether someone who is potent will wish to lie in bed with a woman all the time. After all, people who have a perfectly healthy stomach, intestinal tract, liver, pancreas, etc., do not eat continuously. In other words, perhaps potent men would find it much more interesting to spend time at their laboratory or at the library, instead of satisfying their libido.

> *'Can't we expect that without doubt, their joy of living will return with their ability to enjoy themselves?' professor Gurrie wonders.*
> *'Or go away again just as quickly, because who are these potent men of eighty supposed to enjoy themselves with? With eighty-year-old women? Don't forget that a concoction that makes women of eighty look eighteen again, has yet to be discovered,' answers Dingelam.*

W.F. Herman's message is clear: elderly men can also lead a happy life without erections. Furthermore, there are probably very few young ladies who are interested in potent greybeards.

Venous occlusion and other 'solutions'

Occluding the penile veins was the first surgical treatment for impotence. A sixty-six-year-old impotent widower, who received insufficient benefit from Spanish Fly, was the first victim in 1895. The operation was performed under local anaesthetic with cocaine.

Several years earlier, an Italian doctor had reported occluding the penile veins. He injected a caustic fluid into a varicose vein in the penis of a thirty-year-old man who had been impotent all his life. On the fifth day after the treatment, it appeared that the patient had managed to have coitus five times.

In 1908 a famous American urologist from Illinois explained that the favourable outcome of occluding the veins of the penis was the result of impeding the out-flow of blood so that the penis temporarily became larger. He said: 'The larger the penis after the treatment, the greater the impression made on the patient. He believes that the operation has been a success and he regains his self-confidence. The good results are often permanent, even after the out-flow has returned to normal in the course of time.' Despite his optimistic words, the technique was soon forgotten. The long-term results were terrible. Nevertheless surgeons continued to perform the operation until 1953. Thousands of men were subjected to the knife.

In the framework of their developmental thinking, a number of urologists introduced the same technique in the mid 1980s, once again to the disappointment of the men who underwent the procedure. It is a pity that so few doctors are interested in the history of their profession.

After 1920, somatically-orientated doctors in Holland chose to ignore the problem of impotence, while their colleagues in the neighbouring countries as Germany and France remained active. Various theories were developed about the anatomy and physiology of the erection. Experiments using, for example, connecting rods and Magdeburg hemispheres were performed to model the mechanism. In the therapeutic field, physicians had not come any further than prescribing the earlier-mentioned testosterone preparations. In the *Dutch Journal of Sexology* from December 1992, there was a description of how papaverine and yohimbine had been used to treat men with impotence in 1921. At that time people also believed that papaverine and yohimbine increased their sex drive. These substances were combined into PYT (papaverine-yohimbine-tartrate) by a German researcher.

The PYT compound was used extensively in animal experiments. According to the researcher, tomcats showed 'typical heat behaviour' after its systematic administration. In rats that had been put under general anaesthetic, there was 'maximum venous dilatation in the lower pelvic area'. It was also established how large the doses needed

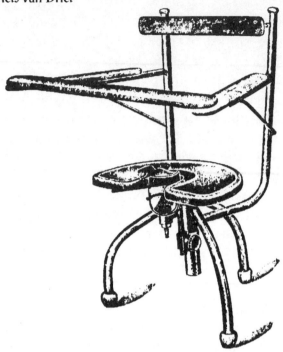

Figure 6: The chair in which the testicles could be stimulated with faradic electricity (1923)

to be to kill a cat, frog, rabbit and mouse. Human male impotence cost a great many animals their lives in this way! Without their knowledge, male syphilis patients were the first human guinea pigs. There were no medical ethics committees at that time. Unfortunately, the results of the study were never published.

The French physician Courtade, along with many others at that time, believed that the application of various types of electricity - faradic or galvanic - to various locations - head, sacrum, lumbar spine - would cure impotence. In the case of impotence caused by prostatitis, they inserted an internal rectal electrode.

Diathermy of the testicles was the next step. It was hoped that slightly raising the temperature of the testicles would increase testosterone production. A special chair was developed for this purpose. A hole at the front of the seat made it possible to hang the scrotum in a glass of saline solution - then the electrical stimulation could begin. Three or four times per week for one month was sufficient. They also knew at that time that a long-term increase in temperature could reduce sperm production.

Convinced that the traditional psychotherapeutic approach often had little effect, the English psychiatrists Russell and Lowenstein used so-called coitus training equipment from 1940 to 1960.

The penis was splinted, so that a man would be able to have coitus even with a limp penis. The equipment was designed in such a way that the outer end could be fastened as close as possible to the underside of the scrotum. When the bolts were tightened, it was important to make sure that no pubic hair was caught. The other end was positioned around the penis so that the scrotum hung totally free and the glans was supported by a sort of ring. The ring was made of ebonite and had five metal plates on the inside.

The theory was that the acidity and humidity level of the penis

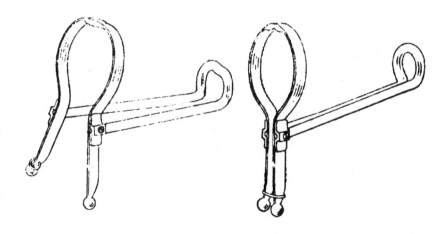

Figure 7: Coitus training equipment developed by psychiatrists (1947)

would generate a small electric current and provide effective impulses to the penis. The aim of the equipment was to break the vicious circle of fear-of-failure and impotence. Apparently, it was already clear in those days that certain men could not be motivated by any kind of psychotherapy. At the same time, this mechanical therapy for impotence reflects how terror-stricken men are of this complaint.

Another, somewhat similar solution is the artificial penis, a more or less realistic imitation. Some women do not approve. The use of a dildo - the stylish name for an artificial penis - is as old as the human race. In the previous century, they sold like hot cakes in all the capital cities of Europe. Clay, paper, wax - anything was used as a raw material. Even today, nice, aesthetically-sound artificial penises are for sale. When using such a device, it is obvious that attention will need to be paid to hygiene. It is recommended to use a lubricant. Full penetration with an artificial penis is not necessary and may even be very undesirable.

High tech: old wine in new bottles

Over the past ten years, urological interest in impotence has increased spectacularly. This is a positive development for various reasons. For example, more attention is being paid to the sexual consequences of surgery. In addition, it has become apparent that physical abnormalities play a role in impotence more often than sexologists originally thought. Also, diagnostic and therapeutic techniques to treat impotence have increased dramatically.

On 25 June 1980, purely by accident, the French vascular surgeon Ronald Virag discovered that injecting papaverine directly into the penis caused an erection. He did not publish this finding until 1982 (in *The Lancet*). Since the 1960s, papaverine has been used during vascular surgery to cause as much dilatation as possible of blood vessels that need to be stitched together. In other words, this medication is another golden-oldie. Just like opium, it is made from the poppy, but it is not the least bit addictive. During a vascular operation, Virag accidentally injected papaverine into the wrong blood vessel, and afterwards the unsuspecting patient was saddled with an erection that took many hours to subside. This gave Virag the idea of teaching impotent patients to inject papaverine into their penis.

During the Second World War, military surgeons used the penis to administer large quantities of blood quickly and efficiently to soldiers in deep shock (i.e. the condition of circulatory collapse). If a patient is in shock, it is often very difficult to find a vein for an infusion line in the arm or leg, because the veins have collapsed and can no longer be seen or felt. If the infusion into the penis was adjusted to drip too rapidly, an erection occurred.

Intrapenile injection therapy (the man injects his penis with a vascular dilator) is therefore derived from military surgical practice and from an 'error' during an operation. Two old wines in one new bottle, combined by a French vascular surgeon!

In 1983, the urological world was extremely startled by a presentation that the eccentric English professor Brindly made on this method at a congress. He had been performing research into the effects of

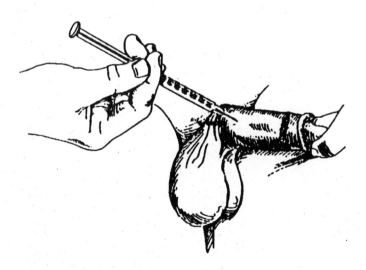

Figure 8: Intracavernous injection

intrapenile administration of phentolamine. It is a vascular dilator (just like papaverine), but it works differently. He made his presentation at the American urological congress in Las Vegas. Usually, speakers at such a congress arrive in suit and tie. However, Brindly turned up in a pair of shorts and training shoes. He started to inform his audience about the results of his studies. About a quarter of an hour later, he interrupted his speech with the announcement that he was getting an erection. The audience was naturally very surprised, particularly when he lowered his shorts and went on to give the people sitting in the first two rows a close look and even invited them to touch it... He told them that immediately before the start of his presentation, he had given himself an injection. The conferees won't forget that presentation in a hurry!

At present, prostaglandine E_1, moxisylyde, phentolamine, a combination of papaverine and phentolamine or a combination of phentolamine and vasoactive intestinal polypeptide are used for the self-injections, the latter being the newest combination. Prostaglandine occurs naturally in the body, whereas papaverine and phentolamine are derived from plants. The dosage required depends on the cause of impotence. It is effective almost immediately and lasts for fifteen to thirty minutes. Depending on the degree of stiffness and the duration, the dosage can be adjusted in steps. A gradual increase in dosage is the preferred approach. This is usually done in consultation with the treating urologist. The aim is to achieve an erection duration of sixty to ninety minutes. If the duration is shorter than this, the man may have to interrupt loveplay for another injection. This makes the process even more unnatural. After ejaculation, the erection does not subside immediately in all patients. An injection into the penis is not painful. Only penetrating the skin is a bit sensitive. Injection of the fluid itself is not painful, because it is quickly diluted by the blood present at the injection site (just as with an injection into a vein). In contrast, an injection into the muscle of the buttocks is painful, because the muscle tissue has to 'make room' for the injection fluid and pain receptors are stimulated. Self-injection into the penis should not be performed more

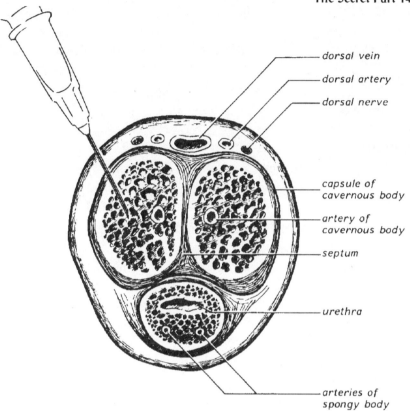

dorsal vein

dorsal artery

dorsal nerve

capsule of
cavernous body

artery of
cavernous body

septum

urethra

arteries of
spongy body

Figure 9: Cross-section of the penis with the injection needle correctly
inserted

than once to twice a week.

Occasionally, the application of injections to the penis can cause a
persistent, usually painful erection (priapism). The blood is trapped in
the cavernous bodies and can no longer circulate, thus there is a lack
of oxygen. If this is not dealt with promptly, the tissues in the
cavernous bodies will suffer permanent damage.

Over the past few years, prostaglandine E_1 has found increasing
application. In contrast with other compounds, it involves less risk of

an erection that continues for too long.

Naturally, papaverine has also been applied to women. Gynaecologists were very eager to test it on anorgasmic women by injecting it into their labia majora, so that whatever else, some degree of moistening would develop. The technique was unsuccessful. No orgasms occurred.

Viagra

It remains curious that at the time we were able to send the first men to walk on the moon, absolutely nothing was known about the mechanism of penile erection. Scientific research did not start until after the introduction of injection treatment. One thing was clear to the learned community: a pill had to be developed as quickly as possible, because many men found an injection painful and it tended to spoil love play. Not the research of scientists, but pure coincidence led to Viagra. During the testing of a new drug for angina pectoris (pain in the chest caused by stenosis of the cardiac arteries) some subjects experienced 'spontaneous' erections.

Viagra led to us finding out more about the mechanism of erection. The nerves produce signals which release nitrogen oxide. This substance alerts the smooth muscle cells in the cavernous bodies.

A good erection is characterised biochemically by a balance between the substance cyclic GMP and the enzyme PDE. Once this situation has become well-balanced, the relationship between in-flowing and out-flowing blood will have reached such a level that an adequate erection can occur. Viagra affects one of the receptors for the enzyme PDE. This enzyme is found all over the body, which also explains the potential side-effects: headaches, blocked nose, dizziness, a full feeling in the stomach and temporary problems with seeing colours.

The recommended dose is 50 mg, not more than once a day. It is best to take the medication one hour before the (planned) sexual encounter. Depending on the result and the side-effects, the dose can be increased to 100 mg after the first time, or decreased to 25 mg.

Viagra has proved effective in a large number of cases: in men with spinal cord lesions an erection occurred in 83%, in depression 76%, hypertension 68%, diabetes 57% and after radical removal of the prostate because of prostate cancer 43%. These are high percentages, which does not alter the fact that particularly diabetes patients have to rely on so-called 'second line' treatments, such as injections, the vacu-pump or an erection prosthesis.

Another treatment method comprised inserting a prostaglandin pessary into the urethra. It was discovered that this medication was absorbed into the cavernous bodies through the wall of the urethra. Obviously a less painful method than an injection. This administration method (MUSE) was accepted in the USA in the spring of 1997. MUSE stands for Medicated Urethral System for Erection. Unfortunately the long-term results of the treatment method turned out to be disappointing.

Not surprisingly, Viagra received more attention than MUSE. Reports started to appear on Viagra from all over the world at the end of 1997. The price of the manufacturers' shares rose rapidly. Viagra also received social renown in another way. Animal protectionists felt that Viagra should be received with an enormous cheer. According to them, the medication offered new chances of survival for many species of animal that are threatened with extinction. Animals that were killed in retarded countries because of the belief that they have potency-increasing qualities. Some animal protectionists even went as far as suggesting that a relief fund be set up so that free shiploads of Viagra could be sent to these countries!

Regarding the question of how Viagra will affect female sexuality, a German sexologist said: 'it is very likely that, even more than before, women will be faced with the egoistic, narcistic aspects of male sexuality'. According to him, it does not matter whether a man takes a pill because he really has a problem, or whether he takes one as a pep pill: women will not be impressed by these 'theatrics'. In any case, it will not strengthen their sexual desire. Elderly women might feel cornered if their partner starts to use erection pills, because they are simply fed up with sex and have already given up the practise.

As early as the nineteen seventies, feminists propagated that old-fashioned coitus was definitely not an effective means of bringing a woman to orgasm. 'The radical hard core immediately banned sexual intercourse: a dull, woman-unfriendly and objectionable activity', according to the reminiscences of a Dutch feminist in her column in a feminist monthly magazine. 'Not only then, but also now, women are searching for men who excel in the art of bringing enjoyment. The tide seems to have turned. Sex pills appear on the market that do not keep a man's hand muscles supple, but keep his penis longer in erection. And what sort of wonderful things can he do with it? Just go in and out. In and out, in and out, in and out', wrote this feminist. In her opinion, Viagra will make it even more dull than ever in bed.

Another feminist made an association between Viagra and silicone breast implants. 'What the silicone breast is for a woman, is the Viagra pill for a man. Both remedies are aimed at achieving perfection, albeit in different areas. Women who have silicone breasts implanted do so on the basis of decorative considerations - in extension of a new sofa lies the acquisition of new breasts. Men who queue up for Viagra pills do so on the basis of the need to achieve and the display of power. Because they cannot stand it that there are areas in their lives that do not lend themselves easily for control. Men are not usually fired with enthusiasm about silicone breasts; women will shrug their shoulders at the delights of the Viagra ecstasy: a man who gets an erection from strips of tablets, lost his sex-appeal long ago'.

At the end of the second millennium, Viagra might be an enormous breakthrough for the rhinoceros and a group of men with erectile dysfunction, but among women, the medication has met less enthusiasm. Viagra and other oral drugs as apomorphine will make 'sex on prescription' possible. Has male utopia become reality?

Inspired by the Penile Bone

The first surgical implantation of a penis prosthesis took place in 1936. To reconstruct a penis amputated during trauma, the plastic surgeon Bogoras used a piece of rib cartilage. He used cartilage because he had observed that many male mammals have a penile bone. Possessors of such a bone, called a baculum or *os penis*, include the whale, dolphin, walrus, otter, bear, martin, badger, squirrel, wolf, dog and monkey. In some species of animal, e.g. the spider monkey, the females also have a clitoris bone.

In 1951, W.R. Bett wrote an extensive article about the *os penis*. In the whale, the bone is about two metres long, with a circumference of forty cm at the base. As species climb higher up the evolutionary ladder, the bones becomes smaller. In the walrus it is only fifty-five cm and in the monkey, one or two cm. So far, there is no evidence that homo sapiens have ever had such a bone.

The position and form of the *os penis* differ from one species to another. In the dog it forms a canal for the urethra. In the bear and wolf, it is indispensable for mating. It takes all sorts of forms. In the racoon it is s-shaped, while in the bat it is forked. The squirrel's has a sharp hook, which according to some experts, is used to breakthrough the hymen; others believe that it is used to remove so-called mating plugs. A mating plug consists of sticky residual sperm, which temporarily glues-up the vagina of the female squirrel, to prevent other males from mating with her.

The *os penis* of the otter is characterised by its extreme hardness. Healed penis fractures have been observed in these animals. When male otters fight, they aim their powerful jaws and sharp teeth at the penis of the opposition. Sometimes they obviously manage to break the other otter's *os penis*!

The *os penis* has also been mentioned in the popular literature. Henry Miller uses it as a metaphor for the hardness of his penis in *Tropic of Cancer*. He was the first serious, modern author who wrote honestly about his turbulent love life. Miller used savory language:

O Tania, where now is that warm cunt of yours, those fat, heavy garters, those soft, bulging thighs? There is a bone in my prick six inches long. I will ream out every wrinkle in your cunt, Tania, big with seed. I will send you home to your Sylvester with an ache in

your belly and your womb turned inside out. Your Sylvester! Yes,
he knows how to build a fire, but I know how to inflame a cunt. I
shoot hot bolts into you, Tania, I make your ovaries incandescent.
Your Sylvester is a little jealous now? He feels something, does he?
He feels remnants of my big prick? I have set the shores a little
wider. I have ironed out the wrinkles. After me you can take on
stallions, bulls, rams, drakes, St. Bernards [...]

This fantasy is not meant to be degrading for the woman. On the contrary, it reflects the oh so transparent anxiety of modern man: sexual envy and fear of impotence.

The use of cartilage as a penis prosthesis did not prove to be an adequate solution in the long-term. It was gradually reabsorbed. Therefore, in the nineteen fifties, synthetic penis prostheses were developed. Initially they were implanted in the penis, but outside the cavernous bodies. Thousands of years ago, this had also been attempted in China - you guessed it - with chicken bones. After a while it appeared that the chicken bone wore its way through the skin. The same happened with the first subcutaneous penis prostheses. Consequently, the technique was changed. In 1960, Beheri described a method that is still being used today: two cylinders are implanted into the cavernous bodies, which in effect, fill them up. In the process, the tissue of the spongy body is lost permanently.

Implanting a penis prosthesis is an irreversible procedure, because the man's own cavernous bodies are forfeited. Despite optimal patient/partner education, it is generally difficult for a couple to imagine what it will be like to live with a penis prosthesis. It is almost impossible to persuade a patient who has had the operation, to come to the clinic and talk about it - generally the most effective patient education method. False shame plays an important role in this. Therefore, the topic remains hidden behind a mist of secrecy. Similar circumstances are described in the novel *The Story of R* by the Italian authoress Gaia Servadio. Her leading woman, a rich business woman, tells her young lover the following about a penis prosthesis:

I shouldn't be telling you this, but he has just got back from Bulgaria where he had an operation on his... er... you know what I mean! There is a small pump inside him that, with a bit of manoeuvring, makes it stand up. They say it is a painful operation, but a lot of people have it done. I mean, what else can you do? Once a man has reached seventy, he knows all there is to know about sex, but he is no longer capable of doing anything with it. It's different for women, am I right or not?'

'But after the pump has been inserted, what can the man do? Can he still reach orgasm?'

He can, because reaching orgasm does not depend on having an erection. Experience shows that an orgasm with an erection is highly appreciated by the majority of men. After implanting a prosthesis, the orgasms often improve.

There are various types of prosthesis on the market. The so-called semi-rigid one consists of two flexible plastic cylinders. One is placed in each cavernous body. From a cosmetic point of view, it is wise to circumcise the patient as well. After implantation, the penis is persistently in erection, but it is flexible so that it can easily be concealed under clothing and urinating does not cause any problems. The situation can be compared with the flexibility of an old-fashioned desk lamp.

The much more expensive inflatable prosthesis has the advantage that the penis is limp when 'at rest' and it imitates a natural erection. The prosthesis consists of two cylinders that can be inflated. Just like the semi-rigid prosthesis, the cylinders are implanted into the cavernous bodies. The length of the cylinders can only be determined during the operation and requires great precision. If they are too long there is a risk that they will breakthrough the capsule of the cavernous bodies. If they are too short there is a risk of the 'Concord phenomenon': the glans hanging downwards in erection. The cylinders in the cavernous bodies are connected to a pump located in the scrotum and to a fluid reservoir located in the abdomen. If a patient wishes to have an erection, he can squeeze the pump and fill the cylinders with the fluid from the reservoir. It takes a bit of practice to perfect this manoeuvre. To make his penis limp again, the patient has to squeeze his penis and press a valve in the pump to allow the fluid to flow back into the reservoir.

Scientific research has shown that a penis prosthesis causes few problems in everyday life. However, a semi-rigid prosthesis cannot always be adequately camouflaged. Tight swimming trunks, for example, are not recommended.

Some men who have received a semi-rigid prosthesis complain about the length of their penis. In erection, it does not grow longer, in contrast with the inflatable type which increases both in length and thickness. Another reason for complaint is not being able to reach orgasm. However, this complaint does not have anything to do with the prosthesis. The fact is that nearly all the operated patients would

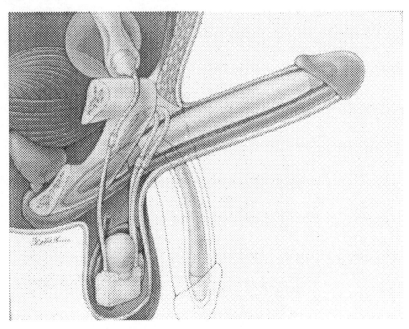

Figure 10: The inflatable erection prosthesis (AMS)

have the operation again. Apparently, even partial recovery of their erectile capacity is experienced as successful symbolic restoration of the damaged feeling of male self-worth.

It is important to gain clear insight into the expectations of the patient and his partner *before* the operation. This is not a job for the urologist alone; a sexologist should also be involved. Unfortunately, we occasionally find out afterwards that it would have been better not to have operated on a patient.

An example from the pre-Viagra clinical practice: a forty-nine-year-old man had been suffering from impotence complaints for some time. On the basis of the results of various tests, the urologist was convinced that the cause was psychological. He sent the patient along to see a sexologist. It soon became apparent that the patient had an unhappy sexual history. He was married at a young age, but divorced a few years later and then started a homosexual relationship. Later he realised that he felt more attracted to women after all. After a fairly rough life, the patient settled into a less turbulent existence. He swore off drink and married a slightly older woman. Unfortunately, this relationship also went wrong. His wife was led astray by the minister from the religious society that he had joined. The patient started afresh with a new relationship, but his penis let him down. And what does he find? The sexologist he consulted could not help him. He was sent back to the urologist with the request to teach him intrapenile self-injections. It soon turned out that this was a big failure. He had bruises on his penis, was complaining of pain, etc.. An (external) vacu-pump did not form a solution either. The patient was very reluctant to go back to the sexologist. His wife refused to go with him. Ultimately, at the insistence of the patient, it was decided to implant a prosthesis. A semi-rigid one, because the urologist did not think that the patient was dexterous enough the handle an inflatable prosthesis and to keep the price low (he too has to stick to a budget). The operation was performed without complications.

During a check-up at the outpatient clinic, the patient expressed his dissatisfaction about the ultimate results of surgery. Not surprisingly, he had not informed his daughter about the operation. He mentioned that his daughter had been looking at his groin when his granddaughter had been sitting on his knee. He is convinced that his daughter saw 'an erection' and has been avoiding him ever since. It proves impossible for him to take the edge off the argument. Perhaps it would be better not to implant any more semi-rigid prostheses.

The Vacu-pump

Not only by implanting an erection prosthesis, but also by using a so-called vacu-pump in combination with a constricting ring, it is possible to simulate a more or less natural erection. A constricting ring has been used as an aid for centuries. Four hundred years ago in Japan, penis rings formed part of the contents of so-called love boxes. The Bedouins used the dried eyelids of goats. The eyelashes were intended to provide extra erotic stimulation and sexual arousal for the woman during coitus. Nowadays such rings are still being sold at sex shops.

Vacuum equipment has been available for almost one hundred years. The version developed by Zabludowsky was described in the *Handbuch der Sexualwissenschaften* (*Handbook of Sexual Sciences*) by the German psychiatrist Albert Moll published in 1912.

Vacuum erection equipment did not start to receive attention in medical circles until fairly recently. Sex shop owners were obviously very interested in them and they are still selling them.

A modern vacu-pump comprises a cylinder, a pump and a band or ring. Fortunately, a real vacuum, i.e. a space entirely devoid of air, etc., is never achieved; otherwise the cylinder would be completely filled with a bleeding penis and testicles. 'Negative pressure' equipment would be a better name. The cylinder is closed at the top and open at the bottom where the penis is inserted; then the base of the cylinder is pressed in an air-tight fashion against the pubic bone. In some cases it is advisable to shave off the pubic hair around the penis. The pump

Figure 11: The vacu-pump according to Zabludowsky (1912)

is attached to the closed end of the cylinder, where it is used to remove the air and thus create a negative pressure. This causes blood to be sucked into the cavernous bodies and an erection occurs. About 120 mm Hg pressure is required: the pressure in the cavernous bodies during erection. In reality more pressure is necessary, because when the penis is sufficiently stiff, the ring that has been placed ready around the opening of the cylinder, is rolled off onto the penis to prevent blood from escaping from the penis, but some always leaks out. The resulting loss of pressure is relatively high. Therefore, usually a negative pressure of about 200 mm Hg must be achieved. Once the constricting ring is in place, blood can no longer escape from the cavernous bodies. On the underside of the ring there is a small opening, so that the urethra is not closed off completely and ejaculation is not hindered. The ring must not be left in place for longer than thirty minutes. It is important not to fall asleep while it is still in place!

Stopping the flow of blood sometimes makes the penis turn a bluish colour. Very tiny pin-point bruises might also appear. It is not unusual under these circumstances for the penis to feel cold. A woman once formulated the feeling as follows: 'It was like making love to an ice-rabbit'. The penis might also 'wobble' at the base, which can make penetration of the vagina somewhat difficult.

It speaks for itself that the use of a vacu-pump during sexual intercourse stands and falls with the presence of a sympathetic and understanding woman, who does not make any high esthetic demands regarding the phallus.

Alternatives for the vacu-pump are Viagra (cost: US $7 to $10 a

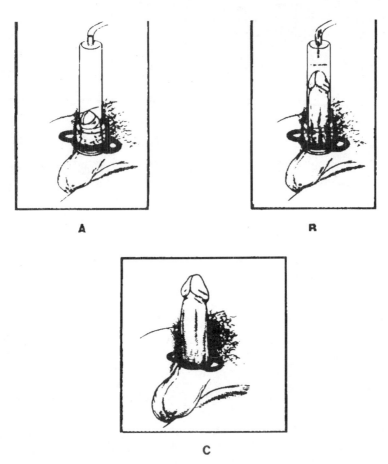

A   R

C

Figure 12: The vacu-pump with a rubber constricting ring at the base of the penis

time, the MUSE-pellet into the urethra (cost $15 to $18 a time), self-injections into the penis (cost: $4 to $20 a time), or surgical implantation of an internal, inflatable erection prosthesis (cost of materials in 2000 $5,000). If the latter patient has coitus one thousand times before he dies, the cost is also $4 a time. Hardly any patients need to worry about the cost. In Holland, society pays for prosthesis implantation. Sometimes people ask hesitant questions about this. Nevertheless it is important to include the aspect of price when weighing up the advantages and disadvantages of a particular treatment. I have only encountered one patient who raised objections about the cost. He was, what else would you expect, a church minister. Ultimately, he had the operation, with good result.

3

Other Penile Problems

A s people grow older, a great many men notice that they sometimes have more trouble getting an erection or maintaining one. Some believe that this is the end of their sexual role. They think that they are in the penopause. This is perfectly understandable if they were brought up with the idea that sex has something to do with 'fertilisation', or in any case, the capacity to do so. The machine has to function properly, 'otherwise there is no longer any need', is the way it is formulated.

With the passing of time, all men will encounter sexual moderation to some extent, but not all at the same age and/or with the same consequences. A number of them will have dropped sexual activities a long time ago, some completely, some partially. Others remain active until some illness or other more or less strikes them down and they have to take the back track.

Some men associate sex with the struggle against death. Owing to the fact that their organ can no longer stand up to it, they become afraid they are about to lose the battle. Particularly these men are glad to hear from an expert that with advancing years, the penis always becomes less stiff and that it is normal for their penis to let them down now and then. These men usually reject artificial treatment. Their marriage no longer needs to be consummated. The point was to find out whether or not we have reached death's door.

The physical symptoms of the penopause are often accompanied by worrying. The man starts to think about the life he has led: How much have I achieved of all the things I used to dream about? I will have to stay married to this person for the rest of my days. Until my death I will always see the same furniture, the same house, the same street. And until my pension I will have to work my fingers to the bone in that awful job of mine! At this stage, such reflections will often catch a man unawares. He starts to wonder what the future still has to offer. Although his fertility does not come to an end, it is possible that he thinks that his potency is decreasing. This might easily lead to sexual failure in bed.

Sybren Polet wrote about this in his novel *Breekwater* (Breakwater) in 1963. A higher official at an insurance company, called Mr. J.H. Breekwater, begins the penopause and feels, in the course of the story, that reality is slipping away from him. Breekwater passes through just about every phase of humanity: he is afraid of becoming impotent, he dies a couple of times and has an inconsummate affair with his secretary Merel. The novel ends with a hallucinatory repeat of a failed sexual encounter with Merel:

'He won't get big', he said sadly.

'You just take your time', said Merel, 'you'll manage in a minute'.

But he doesn't wait and throws himself with desparation into new embraces, embraces that make the waves expand around him in ever larger circles. He kissed her and stroked her as if his life depended on it.

The young woman beneath him moaned, 'Oh Breekwater!'

She believes my desperation is passion, he thought bitterly. Oh God.

A short while later he crumples exhausted at her side, sweating like a pig. His strength used up for the moment.

A bit further on:

'Oh no, my husband has a little paunch. He better make sure it goes away. No eating sweets and sugar; he must do plenty of sport, rowing, swimming, tennis, morning exercises'.

*Breekwater closed his eyes. He **used** to do a lot of sport; he'd swum and played tennis and he'd walked to work every morning. She knew that didn't she?*

'And such sweet little pubic hairs, just like on the scalp of an red Indian, you should be ashamed of yourself. Go on then, be ashamed.'

He twisted his mouth into a grimace, which luckily she did not see, made a thin noise that was supposed to sound like a laugh. She took a couple of his hairs between two fingers and stretched them out; one of the hairs reached all the way to his navel.

Looser than it used to be, he thought, looser and drier. Hairs that could break because they were so brittle. And the beautiful curls had gone. It was time he went for a friz. With infinite tenderness she took his ill-behaved member in her hand, the one that would not grow bigger, a wrinkly old man, a stubborn gnome that could bring a man the worst defeat of his life.

'It is a puppet', she said, 'a naughty, sweet little puppet. Puppet still has to grow and become big. He has to look into the world with the eyes of a sailor on watch, or a soldier in the army. Left-right is how he has to march, experience adventure, conquer foreign lands'. (She waved his penis softly back and forth while she slapped the little head of the military man against the palm of her hand).

She carefully pulled back the skin from the glans and let the soldier gaze into the world. 'He's still tired,' she said, 'he had to get up so early this morning.' She bit into it softly.

'It won't work, it won't work,' shouted the tortured Breekwater. 'Leave me alone.' And once again he threw himself upon her with the frenzy of a madman.

It is not necessary for men to worry so much if their penis lets them down as they grow older. But that is the crux of the matter. They generally start to worry seriously the very first time it happens. And that creates fear of failure. The man feels guilty and finally looks upon sex as torture.

A Fairy Tale About Growing Old

When God created the world and wanted to grant a life span to all his creatures, the donkey came to him and asked: 'Lord, how long will I live?' - 'Thirty years', was God's answer, 'are you pleased with that?' - 'Well, Lord', the donkey answered, 'that is a long time. Think of my wretched existence: carrying heavy loads from morning till night, burdened with sacks of corn to take to the mill while others eat the bread, and not being urged on by anything other than beatings and kicks! Could you let me off part of that time?' God had mercy and gave him eighteen years. The donkey went away comforted and the dog appeared.

'How long do you want to live?' God asked him, 'the donkey thinks thirty years is too long, but you will be satisfied with that.' 'Lord', answered the dog, 'is that your will? Think of how fast I have to run, my paws will not survive that long; and once I have lost my ability to bark and I do not have any teeth to bite with, what is left for me but to walk growling from one corner to another?' God saw that he was right and gave him twelve years.

Then along came the monkey. 'Am I correct in thinking that you will want to live for thirty years?' God asked him, 'you don't have to work like the donkey or the dog and you are always cheerful. 'Well, Lord', he answered, 'it might seem that way, but the truth is different. If it rains porridge, I don't have a spoon. I always have to do foolish tricks, pull daft faces to make people laugh and if they give me an apple and I bite into it, I find it's sour. So often sadness is hidden behind my jokes! I won't be able to keep that up for thirty years.' God had mercy and gave him ten years.

Finally, along came man. He was happy, healthy and cheerful and asked God how long he would live. 'Thirty years', said God, 'do you think that is long enough?' -'What a short time!', grumbled man. 'Once I have built my house and the fire has been lit in my own hearth; once I have planted trees which blossom and bear fruit and I have started to enjoy my life, it is time to die. Please God, give me a bit longer.' 'Alright, I will give you the eighteen years from the donkey', said God. -'That is not enough', answered man. 'Then you can also have the twelve years from the dog'. -'That's still not enough'. 'Well then', said God, 'I will give you the ten years from the monkey, but that is all.' Man went away, but he was not satisfied.

This is how man lives his seventy years: The first thirty human years, they go past quickly; he is healthy and cheerful, enjoys his work and is glad to be alive. These years are followed by the eighteen years from the donkey: one burden after another is placed upon his shoulders; he has to carry the corn that feeds others, and beatings and kicks are his payment for faithful service. Then come the twelve years from the dog: he sits in a corner, growls and no longer has any teeth to bite with. And when these years have passed, the ten years from the monkey form the conclusion. Then the man is feeble-minded and foolish, does stupid things and provokes ridicule from his children.

This fairy tale by the Grimm brothers was written more than 125 years ago. It reflects how a great many people feel about growing old. The vast majority of young people believe that the above-mentioned, foolish monkeys, no longer partake in sexual activities.

'Old' in front of a four or five-letter word that is slang for penis, makes the insult even worse. A prick is bad enough, but an old one, one that has given up on the job, that is much worse. What man does not fear the moment that his penis, as a sign of his mortality, lets him down for good?

Growing old has sometimes been compared with a game of chess, in which pieces are gradually lost, but in which certain, strong pieces can still govern the field and can even take up a new and powerful position. But every chess player knows what it means to lose your queen in a game. The power of the queen is equivalent to the meaning of eroticism in people's lives. In fact, fearing the loss of eroticism is a major cause of being afraid of growing old.

Something that never changes: as the years go by, sex becomes less frequent. On the basis of various studies, a well-known physiologist-sexologist from Rotterdam, Koos Slob, presented the following percentages: 84% of male fifty-year-olds are still sexually active; 67% of male sixty-year-olds; 43% of male seventy-year-olds and 16% of over eighty-year-olds. In women these percentages are: 76% in 51-60-year-olds, 40% in 61-70-year-olds and 7% in 71-80-year-olds. No data were available on women of older than eighty years.

Nevertheless there are wide individual differences between people as they grow older. Those who have been the most sexually active throughout their younger years are likely to decline most slowly.

Until not so long ago, experts believed that impotence in old age was caused by stenosis of the blood vessels supplying the penis. However, there was no scientific proof. New examination techniques, such as duplex ultrasound, have shown that this is not often the case. It is possible to measure the blood flow velocity in the artery in a cavernous body. There is not usually anything wrong with the inflow of blood; the sole problem is that the cavernous bodies are unable to retain the blood that flows in. There is strong evidence that as a man grows older, the stiffness of his erection decreases because of changes in the structure of the cavernous bodies and the tough membranous capsule surrounding them. This capsule plays a major role in blood retention. It is generally the rule that muscles, tendons and joint capsules become thinner as a person grows older and that they gradually lose their elasticity. This loss of elasticity is also the reason why the penis becomes shorter in old age.

Obviously, there are many factors that can have a negative effect on older men's potency, for example, chronic medication use and disorders such as diabetes. Calcification of the joints in rheumatism can cause pain and limit the range of movement, which impedes coitus. Although a heart attack or stroke does not automatically lead to problems with sexual intercourse, the patient will understandably be afraid of having a repeat attack.

Many men are reluctant to ask their treating physician for advice about sexual functioning after a heart attack. What does it mean 'to take it easy' in this respect? It is highly probable that a decrease in sexual activities will have a negative influence on a man's general state of health. Not surprisingly, after a man has had a heart attack, he will be afraid of overburdening his heart. However, heart patients can have a perfectly satisfying sex life without asking too much of their heart. Driving a car in heavy traffic, playing with the grandchildren or having a heated argument with someone are a much greater burden for the heart than having sex. Studies on the frequency of heart attacks during sexual intercourse have shown that when they occurred, it was often in association with an extramarital affair. Thus, not recommended for heart patients!

Rusting Solid

In his book *Vastgeroest* (Rusted Solid) Guy de Maupassant writes about the body rusting solid in older age. In the story Monsieur and Madame de Courville did not manage to marry the elderly baron Hector Gontran de Coutelier to Berthe Vilers. Initially the baron was very enthusiastic about his proposed bride. She accompanied him on many hunting forays. But when after some time he was asked pointblank whether he would like to marry her, he appeared to be struck dumb. Several weeks later he informed Monsieur de Courville that he did not wish to go through with the proposed marriage and a few months afterwards he made his definitive confession:

> *You know that for almost twenty years I have not lived for anything except hunting. I didn't care about anything else, didn't think of anything else. Consequently, at the moment I was just about to take on certain obligations regarding the lady, I felt certain qualms within myself.*
>
> *You see, since the time that er... Now listen carefully, I am not sure whether I am capable of er... er... you know what I mean...*

Good. You have to realise that for sixteen years I haven't er... the last time that I er... well, you know what I mean.

In this neck of the woods it is not easy to er... you know? And I had other things on my mind. I preferred my rifle, the field and when I got home I was usually too tired to er... er... think about other things, you understand. And that is why, before I er... with the lady... I was afraid. I said to myself: Find out first, imagine that you are no longer able to er... Get me?

The baron decided to go to Paris for a week first and visited a number of ladies of easy virtue. None of them managed to give him an erection. Then he tried eating hot spices, but they only caused him indigestion. He drew his own conclusions and went to confess. While listening to the confession, Monsieur de Courville found it very difficult not to burst out laughing. When he got home he told his wife the story. She did not laugh, but listened carefully and when her husband had finished the tale she said:

The baron is an idiot. He is frightened, that's all. I will write to Berthe immediately and ask her to come here at her earliest convenience. If a man loves a woman, then er.. then such things will always straighten themselves out!

Obviously, men should not attach such exaggerated importance to their erectile capacities. The majority of women only find an erection important in certain contexts - when it is offered tenderly, when it means more than just a warm piece of meat. And if necessary, they can also manage without!

The psychoanalytic Wilhelm Stekel (1868-1940) a disloyal pupil of Sigmund Freud, believed that under certain circumstances, potency could improve as a man grew older. In his opinion, a man's potency did not depend on his age, but on the sexual 'object' that was on offer. In his youth, a man's sex drive is generally stronger and more turbulent. He is less interested in the woman before him, who provides him with adequate satisfaction, and more interested in 'the female' that is to his taste or satisfies his daily needs.

According to Stekel, many men can associate with prostitutes in their younger years, but can no longer do so as they grow older. At an older age, when desire becomes more refined, love gradually leans more towards 'brainwork', and potency improves under certain circumstances. It is only in a sexually harmonious marriage, in which the partners understand each other in an erotic sense, that the wife will answer to the 'refined taste' and the 'cerebral desire'. The man must be able to bring about 'spiritualization'.

Stekel clarifies this with a story about a sixty-two-year-old painter, whose considerably younger wife was 'a strikingly sensible, Juno-like lady of marvellous beauty'. The man had been impotent for twenty years. He did have erections in the beginning, but they always wilted at the very moment he approached his wife. For the past ten years, he had not had an erection at all, not even in the mornings. In addition, he was suffering from nightly spates of anxiety and was afraid of heart problems. The man was unpredictable and often lost his self-control.

His wife was only happy when he was absent. He blamed the situation on his wife. His potency appears to have always been very inconsistent:

You see, doctor, I often couldn't manage to have sex in the normal way when I was a young man. I always needed to be in some sort of danger to be able to accomplish the act. Yes, you might laugh! I have never really been potent in bed, only with my wife at the beginning of our marriage. But if I could fling a girl into a corner, or onto the ground or onto a couch, I never had any problems.

His wife had fallen in love with him because she had admired his paintings so much. She had been one of his pupils, but had given up painting after they got married. When she took it up again, he realised that he did not have any 'feeling' for mediocre lady painters. Upon that she started to criticize his work and sided with an art critic who had made him look foolish. 'Was that before your impotence?', Stekel asked. The patient answered:

Wait a minute. I can remember the precise date of the exhibition. Also the date of the first failure, because it was my wife's birthday and we were in Semmering together. Naturally. I suffered the failure several months later. I wanted to make love to my wife during the day, but she refused. I had my first fit of rage. I could have hit her. That night in bed I was impotent, and I was so angry that I threw the electric lamp on the floor.

During the psychoanalytical treatment, his wife died. Two weeks later he forced himself upon his hunch-backed cook. After a couple of months he sacked her and fell in love with one of his young pupils who worshipped him. With her he appeared to be perfectly potent and could make love to her in the normal way in bed..

Stekel considered this case to be an example of the discrepancy between brutish and 'spiritual' love. Undoubtedly, this man's sexual desires had been brutish and possessive since an early age. Through the spiritual bond with his wife he had managed to distance himself to some extent from such tendencies. However, his sexual potency disappeared when his wife denounced her 'spiritual' admiration of him. Then she too became 'just another silly female' that he would have liked to fling onto a couch.

Priapism

A totally different penile complaint is priapism, the medical name for an erection that lasts for longer than three hours, is usually painful and not associated with sexual arousal. In Greek-Roman mythology, Priapus was one of the lesser gods, of fertility, wine-growing, horticulture and bee-keeping. He was usually portrayed with a gigantic phallus. Originally, he came from Asia Minor. In the eyes of the more cultured Romans, Priapus was a joke. He had been carried over to Greece by the more light-hearted Roman poets in the first century B.C..

The idea was nearly always that Priapus kept guard as a scarecrow or thief-deterrent on a piece of land where a few fruits and vegetables were being grown. His painted/hideous image was chiselled from a rough block of wood. His raw appearance was reflected in his blunt language. Priapus was enormously proud of his large phallus.

The *Priapea* contains a collection of about one hundred obscene erotic verses written in 100 B.C. that conceal nothing about the life and work of the penis. Priapus from the *Priapea* is a sexual glutton, a real Roman macho, that penetrates wherever he can. His sexuality is violent and without feeling. People consider this to be typical of Roman men in Nero's time:

Any woman, man or boy that comes here to rob,
Will feel the consequences with their cunt, ass or gob.

This is the unwavering punishment for stealing from Priapus' garden or orchard. If a woman, a man or a boy commits an offence against the god's domain, then vaginal, anal or oral rape is the penalty.

In the poems, Priapus is offered sacrifices, because not all of it is gross sex. A dancer might dedicate her tambourine or castanets to him, in the hope that her audience will remain just as enthusiastic as Priapus himself. A prostitute might offer a considerable number of wooden penises, one for each man she has 'entertained' the evening and night before.

Priapism can occur as a side-effect of self-injections into the penis, but it can also be caused by leukaemia, malignant tumours in the lower abdomen, the use of certain psychopharmaceuticals and sickle cell anaemia. In the latter disease, the red blood cells are deformed. They resemble sickles. Therefore it is fairly easy for the blood to form clots, especially where the blood is flowing slowly. This occurs for instance in the penis during an erection, particularly at night when an erection might last for twenty minutes. Young men with sickle cell anaemia are prone to priapism; sickle cell anaemia is very uncommon in white populations.

Treatment comprises injecting a vasoconstrictor directly into the penis. If that does not help, then an immediate operation is necessary, in which a by-pass is made to a vein in the groin so that the blood can drain away freely. If that does not help either, then the cavernous bodies will gradually fill with connective tissue and feel 'woody'.

This happened not so long ago to a man still in his late thirties, who developed priapism after taking a certain medication to treat depression. Unfortunately, it appeared that not all doctors are aware of the correct treatment for priapism. Immediate intervention is of major importance, preferably within six hours of developing this painful erection. The man went to his general practitioner who was not very accommodating. He was prescribed an incorrect medication and the doctor did not even bother to discuss the case with a specialist.

Ultimately, the patient sent in a claim to the doctor's insurance company. But in Holland, damages had never been paid before. The solicitor therefore consulted with his colleagues abroad. What did he find? In the United States, this sort of case is awarded about £140,000, in England about £57,000 and in Germany about £23,000. Unmistakable culturally-orientated differences. This patient could be expected to receive about the same as in Germany.

The Curved Penis

The name of marquis Francois Gigot de la Peyronie, personal physician of the French King Louis XV, is associated with a very remarkable penile abnormality. De la Peyronie was the first to describe an ailment in which the penis was curved or angulated in erection owing to the development of a dense fibrous plaque in the wall of one of the cavernous bodies. At the affected site, there is no elasticity and the penis becomes curved. A curved penis can also be the result of congenital asymmetry of the cavernous bodies. Then the penis will have always been curved in erection. The prevalence of this congenital asymmetry is estimated to be about six per thousand male births.

Peyronie's disease (fibrous cavernositis) is chiefly encountered in men aged between fifty and sixty years. With regards Peyronie's disease, men are not keen on owning up. The symptoms are pain, insufficient stiffness in erection or difficult *intromissio vaginalis*, in other words the penis can penetrate the vagina only with a great deal of effort. In addition, having sex with a penis that is shaped like a boomerang can be very painful for the woman. However, the situation is not always as bad as it seems and many women find a curved penis most interesting. One of the central figures in the novel *Het Feest der Liefde* (The Feast of Love) by the young writer Ronald Giphard, had the following to say about it:

> *Besides the advantage that a curved prick has in the mechanics of sexual intercourse, the emotion he calls up in young girls is beyond dispute. I remember once that I saw the hard prick of a pretty sulky chap and afterwards in delight and suddenly in love I shouted: 'Gee! Dylan, what a sweet little thing! I call this the mongol-effect'. Perfect, that's not much fun, that's boring, that's for fascists. Slightly flawed, no problem, that's the way I see it.*

The cause of Peyronie's disease is still unknown. Marquis de la Peyronie sent his patients to Barega, a health resort in the Pyrenees mountains. Not such a bad idea really in the knowledge that in the majority of cases, the ailment heals spontaneously in the course of time. However, the patient's penis will never become perfectly straight again.

If the penis is still very curved one year after the disease was discovered, then there is a good reason to perform surgical correction. There are two techniques: (1) the fibrous tissue is removed and the defect is covered with skin (or a venous graft) from another location, for example from the groin; (2) nothing is done to the fibrous tissue, but the operation is performed on the healthy side of the penis where, with the aid of so-called 'reef knots', the penis is pulled straight. A major disadvantage is that the penis becomes slightly shorter, but a considerable advantage is that there is very little risk of impotence occurring after the operation. This does not apply to the former technique, in which the fibrous tissue is removed. I have a strong preference for the 'reef' method, because there is very little risk of causing unnecessary damage.

Hypospadias

Hypospadias is a developmental abnormality in which the male urethra opens on the underside of the glans, or on the penile shaft or even on the scrotum, instead of the top of the glans. The outer end of the urethra is poorly developed and there is no foreskin on the underside of the glans. In erection it is not unusual for such a penis to be curved. About one in three hundred men have this abnormality. Hypospadias is very probably caused by slight testosterone deficiency in the sixth to thirteenth week of pregnancy.

In order for the patient to be able to urinate standing up and to perform adequately sexually, the urethra will need to be reconstructed surgically and the penis straightened. In the past, boys were not operated on until they were somewhat older, but nowadays urologists generally prefer to operate at the age of two years. The latter approach causes the least psycho-trauma. A new section of urethra is made from the inside of the foreskin. If the boy has already been circumcised, a piece of mucous membrane from inside the cheek can be used.

The scars, the relative shortness of the penis, the necessary circumcision and the abnormal shape of the glans mean that some patients are not satisfied about the result of the operation, particularly during puberty, whereas the urologists who have performed the surgery usually are. After all, they know that their means will always be limited. Doctors cannot do it better than Our Dear Lord.

It is important to explain carefully to the patient that surgical correction of hypospadias will not lengthen the penis. Particularly adolescent or adult hypospadias patients who present with complains about a small penis should be offered sexological counselling. In some cases, a penis lengthening procedure might be considered.

An extremely strange form of hypospadias is *mika*, an initiation ritual that was practised until the beginning of this century in male pubescent inhabitants of the Mangaia island in the Pacific Ocean. With a small incision, the urethra was split open from the outer end to the scrotum. 'Mika' therefore means 'terrible ritual'. The idea was to prevent semen from entering the vagina during sexual intercourse. A rather gross means of birth control! The aboriginals also had the same custom. It is a wonder that these tribes ever managed to reproduce in those days.

Occasionally, a urologist is obliged to *create* hypospadias surgically. Joost Zwagerman wrote about this is his novel *Vals licht* (Artificial light). The prostitute Tanja talks about one of her clients, called *Stumpy*:

> *Only Stumpy had earned his name for another reason than he thought. Stumpy's penis was not extremely small by nature.*
>
> *Roaring with laughter, Tanja explained to him that in the sixties, a car accident had saddled her with a client with an amputated, stub-like extrusion. His glans, which had been ripped and pulverised by piece of broken glass, could not be repaired by any surgical means. Poor, poor Stumpy ... Fortunately, a team of doctors had been able to make a groove that led to Stumpy's urethra. They had then inserted a transparent plastic tube, about the size of a drinking straw, which protruded slightly from his afflicted worm-shaped genital organ.*
>
> *'When he had an erection, it looked just like a banger, complete with touch-paper', said Tanja. She gasped for air and shrieked with laughter.*
>
> *Sometimes urologists have even gone as far as to reconstruct the outlet of the urethra in the perineum between the scrotum and anus, as a last resort after a number of unsuccessful urethral interventions. Men who have been treated in this way are forced to urinate the female way: crouching or sitting.*

Phimosis And Circumcision

A completely different, but common penile abnormality is phimosis: constriction of the foreskin. Nearly all new born boys have some degree of phimosis with adhesion, which usually disappears spontaneously. If phimosis is not treated, urine and smegma can accumulate between the glans and the inside of the foreskin and cause inflammation. Urination becomes painful and the little boys are afraid to urinate. Nevertheless it is not always necessary to operate, because the foreskin can usually be pulled behind the glans and after the application of a little vaseline, it can be rolled back. If this is repeated regularly, the opening will stretch and become wide enough. A doctor can teach the mother or father to do this. If the foreskin will not stretch, then an operation is necessary. The patient will be circumcised.

World-wide, circumcision is performed much more often on ritual-religious grounds. Circumcision was first mentioned in ancient Egypt. Originally, the Egyptians constituted countless nomadic tribes in Middle and Northern Africa. When they settled in the Nile valley, they brought their religion and associated rituals. We can decently assume that the Jews and Muslims in their turn adopted the ritual of circumcision from the ancient Egyptians. The Egyptians viewed circumcision chiefly as a politico-psychological symbol of superiority over the neighbouring uncircumcised nomadic tribes, including the Hebrews.

Anthropologists believe that circumcision is a relic from human sacrifice. People made sacrifices to the gods to ensure their protection and benefaction. Absolute adoration was total sacrifice. In order not to have to sacrifice a whole human being, they offered part of the principal organ, the creating organ, a holy force of nature. Many tribes burnt the severed foreskin, just like a human sacrifice. In this way, sacrifice of the foreskin became a symbol of the pact between God and the people. Within Christianity, circumcision was replaced by christening. Within Islam, circumcision is chiefly a sign of purity. Before a male can take part in religious ceremonies, he must be circumcised.

The Dutch Marxist Soep, who forswore Judaism, published an interesting ethnological study on this subject shortly after World War II. He paid much attention to the various initiation ceremonies with circumcision - and in some cultures clitorectomy - in relation to the meaning of puberty. This is the transition from childhood to sexually mature early manhood (or womanhood), a sort of rebirth. Soep gives a lively description of a circumcision ceremony of the Ubangi Charistam tribe from former French Congo:

They spread a strong odour. Their tiredness, turned into sweat, ran down over their tattoos. They did not notice the tiredness. They were thinking only of the Yangba, giving their whole attention only to her.

Life is short. All too soon comes the day when a person is no longer even capable of coitus. And doesn't every sun bring us closer to our death? People should be joyful for as long as they can. They danced.

[...]

Ganza... Ganza... Ganza... Ganza...!
Soon we will make you Ganzas,
Ganza... Ganza... Ganza... Ganza.

An old man hung with amulets and armed with a knife appeared before the group of young men. On the side of the young girls, an old woman was waiting. And the older ones who were thronging behind the two elders, giggled as they watched the youngsters dance, who were all too soon to suffer.

Ganza... Ganza... Ganza... Ganza...
Ganza... Ganza... Ganza... Ganza...
Tonight you will become a woman.
And you will become real men.
You will be made Ganzas.
Ganza... Ganza... Ganza... Ganza.

The two elders started to speak:
For one month, for two months you have hidden deep in the forest, chastised and fasting. For one month and another month you have

withdrawn from defiling glances, your bodies have paled, so that death cannot abduct your village. You have only spoken the holy language. You have eaten grass and herbs, far away from defiling eyes.

For one month and another you have slept somewhere, somehow. You have been weaned off laughing and playing.

'N'gakura [God] is satisfied with you. Your ordeal has come to an end. You can play again, laugh, dance, in the fresh air, talk and sleep on your mats.

Very soon you will become men. Very soon you will become women. Just a little while longer and you will become Ganzas.

[...]

The ceremony started.

Carefully the two elders whetted their knives on a flat stone that they had first spat on.

Already the helpers were surging towards the staggering patients with raised sticks. If even the slightest pain caused a boy to collapse on the ground, then he was not worthy of being called a man. Then he had to be beaten and die.

That is the custom.

[...]

The young girls, several were extremely pale, danced around in circles. Regardless of how much they endeavoured not to, they trembled with fear.

The old woman took a few steps forward, called one of the dancers, spread her thighs forcibly, grabbed what she could with both hands, pulled it like it was a rubber liana, and in one sweep - whoosh - cut it off.

Even without turning her head, she threw the warm and bloody flesh haphazardly over her shoulder, so that it sometimes struck someone in the face.

It was all done in the blink of an eye. Once the flesh had landed on the ground, the dogs could dispense with it.

Ganza... Ganza... Ganza... Ganza...
Come to us, women! Come to us, men...!
Now you are Ganzas.

*After the last woman had been cut and the last man circumcised,
each of the operators cleaned their knife. Now the noise reached
its pitch.*

*Everything that had gone before was nothing in comparison. All
the shouting, all the confused dancing, were only preparations for
the last performance: the dance of love, which they only danced on
that night, and it was permitted to overindulge in extravagance and
crime. [...]*

*The toucans laughed frighteningly. Nocturnal birds of prey
circled startled above the Hangba.*

But their cries went unheard in the frenzy below.

Even a literary-minded urologist could not write something like
that. What he or she produces is much shorter. A modern operation
report in a medical file might look like this:

*The parents wish to have their son circumcised for religious
reasons. He received general anaesthetic. Application of iodine
and covered. Stretching of the foreskin. Incision and resection of
the inner and outer sheets (2 cm). Trimming of the inner sheet.
Reconstruction with knotted 4 catgut stitches. Vaseline dressing.
Operation time: 20 minutes.*

In the Dutch popular literature, one can find a literary report on
circumcision in *De Sluier* (The Veil) by L.H.A. Drabbe. In 1906, this
novel was so daring that it was received in complete silence. Not one
single critic ventured to pick up the theme. The title alludes to an
abnormally long, narrow foreskin that was removed shortly before the
central figure got married. In view of the fact that common decency
forbade him from talking about it to his future wife, there were various
complications.

'Now then', answered the doctor, while straightening up from his bent posture and approaching Maurits with a loaded syringe, 'let's see what we can do for you.' And after attentively palpating the member, he warned, 'you must obviously lie very still!'

Maurits felt a small jab, no worse that being bitten by a mosquito, followed by another and another and [...]

'It looks so strange now, doctor', said Maurits.

'Yes, it certainly does, you are quite right, looks funny doesn't it?'

And while jabbing him a couple of times to test whether the anaesthetic was working, he asked, 'Can you still feel it?'

'No, doctor.'

'And this? and this?'

'No, doctor, I can't feel anything.'

'Good, then we have finished the prelude', said doctor Mast who with nimble swiftness inserted a cylindrical tube through the opening of the foreskin to free the swollen tissue [...].

[...]

Maurits is suddenly alert. He sees how doctor Mast, having removed the cylinder, slips one blade of a pair of scissors through the opening and then - just like cutting cardboard - starts to snip. Four, five times the scissors open and close and the sight of that cold, sharp steel cleaving through the weak, swollen flesh makes him feel so awfully faint, although he can't feel anything, that he starts to moan softly [...].

'I don't seem to be bleeding much, doctor,' said Maurits with a timbre of nervous relief in his voice.

'Oh, my dear chap, I'm over the moon, no secondary bleeding at all, it's just like it should be, and may I say, you have a penis fit for an exhibition'.

[...]

Maurits is completely confused. While the doctor is busy again at the table beside him, he sits up and has an inquisitive look at his reproductive organ. After all, he has to see what it looks like. But unfortunately he can't really make it out, that blood-stained stump lying there, with the wide, thick-walled wound gaping. Nevertheless to his joy he discovers the pink opening of the freed glans, that appears to come out and take a quick look around, as if it needs to gasp for air after so many years of imprisonment. Good gracious, he can see it!

Pages long, there is a detailed account of circumcision at the beginning of this century. *De Sluier* is the first phallus novel in the Dutch literature, but above all it is a tragicomic story of fear and false shame.

Nowadays all the sons of professed Mohammedans and Jews and tribes in Africa, Australia, Melanesia and Polynesia (with the exception of New Zealand) are circumcised. The Polynesians perform circumcision to make the organ look clean and strong. They also believe that a circumcised man experiences a more powerful orgasm. Jewish boys are circumcised at the age of eight days, Muslims later, usually before or during puberty.

It is written in the bible that the tradition goes back further than the patriarch Abraham. At the age of ninety-nine years, by the will of God, he was circumcised and by his own hand he used a sharp stone to circumcise his son and all the other males living under his roof (Genesis 17:10-14 and 23-27).

In 1995 a theologist interpreted these passages as follows in the monthly magazine *Child and Sunday*:

Abraham became unified with God and could not therefore remain untouched. The sign of this was circumcision. The union cut into Abraham's flesh, there where it was most vulnerable, it 'circumscribed' his manhood. Circumcision was a continual reminder of the union with God, it was a sign that nothing would become of God's future with only male strength and potency.

Another theologist in the same magazine:

Circumcision is not only the ultimate sign of the union, but it also means 'Be impeccable', as God said to Abraham in verse I. Literally the Hebrew word 'impeccable' means: complete, as one, perfect, faultless. Not that Abraham was forbidden to make any more mistakes and it was not about physical perfection. It means something like: let your conduct be such that you can stand in honesty before God. But union with God sometimes also meant that you had to give something up; it cost you; it hurt! That aspect is reflected in circumcision.

In Arabian culture, circumcision also existed long before Mohammed. The new religion simply adopted the ritual. In the *Koran*, there is not a single text that bears upon circumcision, while in the exegete texts one has to wait until 200 years after the death of Mohammed. Then El Bokhari (810-870), a Persian lawyer and theologist, declared that Mohammed said: five deeds belong to our tradition: circumcision, the removal of pubic hair, the removal of axillary hair and trimming the moustache and nails.

The Jewish writer Philo van Alexandria (25 B.C. - 50 A.D.) was the first to come up with hygienic motives for circumcision.

Paraphimosis can occur if a man has slight phimosis and the foreskin is pulled behind the glans and cannot be rolled back. The glans and foreskin swell up through blood congestion and oedema. Pain and panic are the consequences. Doctors speak in terms of a 'Spanish ruff', after the stiff collar-boards worn by prominent Spaniards in the sixteenth and seventeenth centuries. Paraphimosis can be alleviated by gripping the glans and foreskin in the whole hand and by gradually increasing the pressure until the swollen tissue becomes slack. Usually, this will be followed by circumcision.

As mentioned above, the glans is an extension of the spongy body, the erectile body that contains the urethra. During erection the glans swells, but the internal pressure remains lower than in the cavernous bodies. The outer part of the glans is composed of sensitive mucous membrane, which is normally covered by the foreskin. The foreskin is lined with mucous membrane and has skin on the outside. Owing to the fact that the vagina is also lined with mucous membrane, the penis can slide easily back and forth. Both the glans and the foreskin contain countless highly sensitive nerve endings, which increase sexual pleasure. The foreskin is therefore an important erotic organ. Just stroking the foreskin can lead to ejaculation. The shaft of the penis is far less sensitive. If the foreskin is removed, a sexually-relevant part of the penis is lost. Continual rubbing desensitizes the mucous membrane of the glans.

Every Jewish man may circumcise, but circumcision (*mila*) is usually performed by the *mohel*. The *sandak*, a sort of godfather, holds the child on his lap. The mohel pulls the whole foreskin forward in front of the glans and places the skin into the groove of a small shield. The foreskin is incised across the front of the shield, without any anaesthetic. The wound used to be sucked out by the mohel (*mezizah*), but it appeared that syphilis, tuberculosis, diphtheria (and these days also aids) could be transmitted, thus a suction instrument was introduced. The wound was dusted with mohel flour, a powder made from oak wood. Nowadays a bandage is applied. In the previous century it was customary for the Falaches, a Jewish sect from former Abyssinia, to circumcise stillborn boys before they were placed in a coffin. The intention was to make sure that when they were reborn, they would be recognised as Jews.

Both the Jews and Muslims surround circumcision with prayers and rituals. The Indonesian Muslims call circumcision *sunat*. Sometimes a *doekoen* (village doctor) or priest does the *bong* or *bengkong*, but it is usually done by a layman. On Java the foreskin is cleaved lengthwise. A flat piece of bamboo is inserted between the glans and the foreskin and the foreskin is cleaved lengthwise along the piece of bamboo. As the glans is initially unpleasantly sensitive after circumcision, the boys are placed in cold running water. To protect the glans from rubbing, they wear half a coconut over their penis, held in place by a cord around their waist.

The television film *The Winds of War* showed how foreigners, including Americans, travelled to Berlin through the German lines after the invasion of Poland in 1939. Jews and people with Jewish faces or Jewish names were picked out by the Germans. If there was any doubt, the nazi's looked to see whether the men were circumcised. In the film, an American minister who was travelling in the group, protested about this: 'All Americans are circumcised, me too.' Under pressure from the nazis, many foreskin reconstruction operations were performed in that period. This is also an age-old practice. In ancient Rome, there were Jews who wished to reverse their circumcision owing to certain sanctions. Obviously there were successful methods in those days, because when the law that forbade circumcision was dropped, the rabbis sharpened the criteria that circumcision had to fulfil. The foreskin had to be removed completely, so that there was no remaining tissue for possible later experiments.

Then there is the interesting discussion about 'the marble foreskin of King David'. Michelangelo's famous statue of this Jewish son and heir, has a foreskin. Scientists have ultimately explained that Michelangelo knew exactly what he was doing: King David lived in about 1000 B.C., whereas it was not until after 300 B.C. that the circumcision laws were sharpened. Before that time, only a small rim of the foreskin was removed. And that is exactly what you can see on the statue of David: the foreskin does not completely cover the glans!

At the beginning of this century, the hypothesis was launched in an American journal that the low frequency of cervical cancer in Jewish women was the result of the men being circumcised. Although this assumption could not be confirmed by further scientific research, the reaction was over-exaggerated. Subsequently, the vast majority of American boys were circumcised, usually at hospitals. This so-called 'health circumcision' (circumcision on medical grounds) had already been applied in Victorian England, but that was in an attempt to prevent masturbation. It was not until 1990 that the tide turned with respect to 'health circumcision' in America. An interest group was set up for and by circumcised men. They could not only cry on each other's shoulders, but also exchange experiences about all sorts of methods of reconstructing the foreskin. One technique was to create 'new' tissue by carefully stretching the remnants of the foreskin. Clamps, plasters and elastic bands were used for this purpose. Homosexuals were the pioneers, as is so often the case with this sort of problem. The anticircumcision lobby spread its newsletter *No-circ* from San Anselmo in America. The newsletter contained information about success stories, such as the prohibition to circumcise women, with which the men immediately thought they could close the door against ritual, religious male circumcision. In a statement, the movement emphasized that performing ritual circumcision was a sin against the old medical adage *primum non nocere* (do not cause damage). Even the UN treaty for human rights became involved: nobody would be subjected to torture, or to inhuman or humiliating treatment.

Ritual circumcision places many surgeons, urologists and plastic surgeons (who all perform circumcision) in a dilemma. On the one hand there is the right concerning integrity of the body and soul, and the right of self-determination. On the other hand there is religious freedom with archaic rules and the unjustified fear of cervical cancer and penile cancer. In view of the increasing workload of operating theatres, Dutch hospitals have decided to limit the number of ritual circumcisions. One thing is certain: the majority of health insurance companies cover the cost of the procedure. The Dutch national health service says that on the basis of an implementing order from 1983, they do not in principle cover the cost of circumcision on the grounds of other than medical indication, but practice shows otherwise.

4
Women and Feminism

As a remedy against the temptations of love, the Buddhists thought up a meditation exercise in which they depicted the body of a woman as a bag of filth. Medieval ascetic writers considered a woman to be 'a temple built above a sewer'. At the same time, Church Father Augustine said: 'A woman is the gateway to Satan'. If we take these words literally, then over the years, many men have challenged the kingdom of the prince of darkness! In any case too many for them all to have ended up in hell. Perhaps it is particularly the men who have neglected to engage a woman's pleasure who end up there.

Abnormalities at the gate

Certain physical abnormalities in a woman - abnormalities at the gate - can cause impotence. One of these is adiposity, or obesity. Smit described it in his book: *De Arts voor Gehuwden en Ongehuwden.* (*The Doctor for the Married and Unmarried* in 1810:

> *Aristotle was right: fat ladies possess too little allure, are too cold-blooded, their ovaries are surrounded by too much fat impeding the release of the egg, the tissue-forming lymph is too sticky and thick, and moreover, the fat stomach, through the totally extruding*

182 Mels van Driel

lardaceous promontory, hinders the pleasant deep penetration of the male member. Lean fare, exercise, gardening, short sleep, and activity of the sole are the best advice. Mustard has the most power to melt fat and cause weight loss, but too much weakens the workings of digestion, unbinds the viscousness of the blood, and is harmful to health. In the meantime, people have often seen examples, that plump ladies have many children; delivery, however, is often very difficult for them. As far as the rest is concerned, a cul de Paris, or a well-filled cushion, may lighten the man's work considerably.

Also a vagina that is too narrow - by nature or acquired - can lead to problems. When a gynaecologist operates on a prolapse or such like, he or she will make sure that the vagina remains accessible for at least two fingers. That is about the thickness of the average penis. Smit wrote the following about a vagina that is too narrow by nature:

A too narrow vagina, which is sometimes encountered in very slight, thin women, makes the union painful, unpleasant, fruitless. In one case, in which after scores of attempts over nine months, the able-bodied man could not penetrate any further than the glans, the couple was mutually obliged through the pain to cease any further efforts. Thilenius injected a spoonful of almond oil morning and night, placed a four inch long oil-smeared, and easy to extract piece of fungus into the vagina.

Men who are equipped with an extremely strong glans, may be pleasant for women of experience, but for defloration, and for the pleasure of young innocent girls, these are highly unsuitable. If a young husband encounters such circumstances, then he has leave to make preparations with the finger.

How older women view impotence

Until not all that long ago, older women from the East Bandjoemas tribe had an important role to play. Before a young man could be given permission to marry, he had to pass a sexual examination. The young man had to prove that in his marriage, he could fulfil his reproductive duties. The lady examiner, called a *sentondang*, had to report back to the father. Such a report was usually a simple declaration: 'Father, your son is a complete man.' Or otherwise, if she considered that he had not passed the examination and a retake was required, she might use the words: 'Father, it is still too early to tell.'

What wisdom is expressed by such a culture! The situation is quite different for some western women. A woman cheerfully recounted one day the stories her grandmother had told about the sexual performance of her grandfather. At that time he was almost eighty years old. 'Arie still wants to once a week, you know, but it doesn't amount to much any more. He just about has to shovel him in with a fork'. That is the way that Dutch grandmothers talk to their granddaughters nowadays... Poor granddad!

A former general practitioner told me about a pleasant widower who made the acquaintance of a sturdy Flemish woman. He married her, but turned out to be impotent. Time and again she laughed at him about it and belittled him in front of everyone. On one occasion she laughingly said: 'Shall I stand on my head, then you can *hang* him in'. The general practitioner referred the man to a renowned sexologist, with a letter of referral in which he had written 'she hardens his limpness.'

Naturally, there are also men who express contempt about their wife's genital region. A patient from a far northern province once said: 'It's only that she needs to pee with it (vulva and vagina) otherwise she would be better off hanging it on the henhouse' (a famous saying in the northern part of the Netherlands, which means 'doing away with something').

The art of seduction

In our culture, men often have the tendency to 'instrumentalize' sexuality. They are more interested in certain body parts than in the woman as a whole. Women are usually more interested in the man as a 'person'. The vast majority of women can only give themselves to a man who has approached her *soul*. It cannot be stated often enough: the majority of women - in contrast with what men think- are not really interested in the penis, not even their sexual partner's. To go one better, some feminists - whether or not lesbians - replaced the penis with a pipet full of semen a long time ago. They are not the least bit interested in prick-orientated men - called 'rammers' in sexological jargon.

Modern man is a poor seducer. Seduction comes before courting. Walking up to a woman and telling her loudly that you think she is 'so tasty', is not seduction. Burying her under piles of letters, telephone calls, bunches of flowers or invitations to candlelit dinners are not seduction either. Even long walks along the beach are not seduction, but they do start to look something like it.

In *De Gaykrant* (The Gay Newspaper) from 1 September 1995, Cees van der Pluym described what it is:

It is creating desire, as a slowly germinating plant for which the seed was planted in the earth unnoticed. Then you cultivate this desire, you give the plant water, but make sure it stays thirsty. You let it grow, fertilise it, trim it and speak sweet words to the buds of blossom, and all that without the plant being aware of it. Then, when the day arrives, the bud bursts open and the blossom turns its face to the light. And see: the plant comes towards you, she trembles with pleasure on your windowsill and offers you everything that you would not have been given if you had asked.

This is real seduction, which not only for many women, but also for many men, is much nicer than sex.

Erick Janssen, a researcher from Amsterdam, asked both men and women study subjects to place a number of 'separate parts' of a sexual encounter (stroking breasts, taking knickers off, kissing, undoing bra, coitus, stroking the penis, etc.) in the correct order according to their idea of what was 'natural'. The answers of the men and women -not unexpectedly- agreed. Then the participants were asked to give a score to each of the 'separate parts', which reflected the subjective level of arousal it involves.

The results showed that the level of arousal in the men ran parallel with the 'natural' order (which the men and women had agreed about). For the women, in contrast, this was not the case at all. Their scores for the parts in which they were required to do something with the penis (fill this in for yourself) in conformity with the 'natural' order, decreased by leaps and bounds! In general thus, women just do not really feel like doing that.

Is the penile erection superfluous then? No, but you would almost think so, especially if you read certain types of women's magazines (Woman's Own, for example). According to these magazines, women have a distinct preference for men who are both empathic and excellent listeners. They should be mad about household chores and the children, while they are sexually faithful and extremely devoted to the tender desires of their wife in bed. They should have a natural aversion to pornography and aggression, not feel the need for power and not find it at all important to win or be proved right. In short, a very bizarre collection of characteristics for the average man. The comical thing about these magazines is, of course, that they sum up the typical characteristics of a woman.

Surveys in women's magazines always confirm the stereotype image that women do not really have much enthusiasm for strong, potent men. 'Making love' or 'screwing' (the choice of word depends on the magazine) therefore have a very low score on a woman's priority list.

According to the Dutch journalist Sarah Verroen, this is nonsense. In a feministic radio programme, she held a survey on the ideal lover. Thirty women from the art world, science world, journalism and prostitution were invited to participate in this - otherwise totally unrepresentative - mini-survey.

The results were striking. In answer to the question as to what women find the most satisfying from a sexual point of view, 29 out of the 30 women chose: 'good and hearty screwing', while one chose 'lengthy sex with plenty of attention for you'. No one chose 'vanilla sex', i.e. sex (like the flavour) that lacks sparkle. In answer to the multiple-choice question as to how the ideal lover should behave in bed, 24 out of the 30 women chose 'bold, knows what he and you want'. 'Dominant and a little brutal' was chosen five times, whereas 'tender and totally orientated towards your wishes' was only chosen once.

Verroen jeered at people's cowardly taste for vanilla sex and made it clear that in any case, some women are very much taken with having sex with a man with a hefty erection. They love the phallus with its male characteristics, such as effectiveness, strength and penetration. According to Verroen, eroticism exists by the grace of broad-mindedness. It is the smouldering flame that unexpectedly flashes in the pan. An erection forms part of this. Several decades ago, the French surgeon, Nicolas Venette (1633-1698) summarised the ruling opinion about the treatment of impotence in one sentence: 'If a woman's hand is unable to make the penis stiff, then all other treatments will be equally unsuccessful'. Nowadays there are supplementary possibilities, but they remain, in any case, artificial.

New impotence

At the beginning of the seventies, reports appeared about 'new impotence'. Partly due to progress in medical science in the preceding two decades, the seventies became the era when the feminist movement wanted equal sexual rights. Women started to make demands regarding coitus. In their case they were not so much interested in the quantity, in contrast with the queen of Aragon (see demanded coitus six times per day), but more in the quality. The annoying part was that many men could not take this and reacted with impotence. The sexologist Lazarus put this into the following frank words:

A number of modern social patterns have given rise to tensions that are directly undermining the sexual life of many young men. The *new genre **sexual freedom**, which is associated with aggression from women egged on by the women's liberation movement, puts the male in a position that he is 'frightened limp'. A sure way to ruin male potency is to turn sex into a sort of competition. It is very discouraging for young inexperienced or sensitive men to hear that the previous lover was absolutely fantastic in bed.*

The world gradually became feminised. Women started to write the rules. Some men did not even know what it meant to be a man any more and became utterly confused. On top of everything else, these feministic women made bizarre demands. One moment the man had to overpower the woman, but the next moment caress her tenderly. But, and here is the crunch, the man himself had to be able to feel when to apply which strategy.

Many men think that they are running the show when they penetrate a woman. 'It is his erection that arouses her'. This almost triumphant thought goes up in smoke when he starts trying to control the tempo, determine which parts of her body are the most sensitive, how he should use his muscles, weight, skin and memory to satisfy her, how to choose the right moment for his orgasm so that it coincides with hers. The man banishes his own enjoyment in order to concentrate on hers. He changes into a hard-working grime, slogging away in the mines.

This is how the above-mentioned feminist, Euridice Kamvisseli describes it in her debut novel: *F/32: The Orgasm*. Ela, the heroin in this curious book, has a tight and greedy sexual organ, which is discussed in an inexhaustible manner. She has a fan club of hundreds of ex-lovers who wear a coloured ribbon around their penis that reflects their position in the strict hierarchy of sexual performance.

Just as liberated women today, witches were accused of causing impotence in the Middle Ages. They achieved this with the aid of a ligature, or lace, taken from the victim's trousers. That is to say they practiced the 'art' of tying a knot in this trouser lace, which rendered the man sexually impotent via a sort of figurative magic. This preferably had to happen simultaneously with the wedding ceremony. The method also involved the witch casting a magic spell, after which she hid the lace. At the same time, the witch threw two coins over her shoulder, which symbolised the non-functional testes. The impotence persisted until the unfortunate victim found the lace. If the lace was not found, then the impotence was permanent. In certain regions of France in the sixteenth century, this ritual caused such severe anxiety psychosis that many bridal couples got married at night or in a neighbouring village in order to avoid having the knot tied.

Jacob Cats mentioned in his *Proefsteen van den trouwring* (Test Stone for a Wedding Ring) how a certain 'Martin Guerre was completely unable for eight or nine years to pay his wife the debt of good intentions; and that because of some sort of ill practice that people in France called the knotted lace'. After he realised, with great relief, that the Netherlands had been spared these evil practices, he gave the following description of the ritual:

> *If during the marriage ceremony, and when the priest joins the young people's hands, someone meanwhile mumbles a few ghostly words, and ties a knot in a lace, he renders the bridegroom unable to enjoy his bride, but also renders the same bridegroom able to enjoy the pleasures of other women.*

Witches were also said to be able cause impotence with the aid of magic potions. In the same way, they could also restore the situation. Witches therefore functioned as excellent sex therapists. Undoubtedly, the same applies to the liberated woman of today. Men are in dire need of these modern witches. In *Opzij* (a Dutch feministic magazine) from October 1992, Anke Manschot stated:

> *It is no longer automatically true that men want to have sex more than their female partner. Or that women stare at the ceiling and make shopping lists during sex. Women want to have an orgasm,*

preferably a couple of times in succession, just like so beautifully conjured up in women's magazines. And now of all times, men fail more and more often in bed. Bury their head sooner in a book than in her bosom.

In the feministic confessional literature from the sixties, men were often laid into unmercifully. In her best seller *Fear of Flying* the American feminist Erica Jong writes off her penis envy and puts extra emphasis on the fantastic characteristics of female genitals. She makes a 'soft touch' into a 'limp prick'. She uses this hard description time and time again. She says that she has always been a feminist. The greatest difficulty for Erica is how she can make her feminism agree with her unappeasable hunger for male bodies. That is not easy. Besides, the older she gets, the clearer it becomes to her that men are basically terrified of women. Some secretly, others openly. What is more poignant than a liberated woman finding herself eye to eye with a limp prick? In her eyes, all history's greatest issues pale by comparison with two key items: the eternal woman and the eternal limp prick. A fragment:

*The ultimate sexist put-down: the prick which lies down on the job. The ultimate weapon in the war between the sexes: the limp prick. The banner of the enemy's encampment: the prick at half-mast. The symbol of the apocalypse: the atomic warhead prick which self-destructs. **That** was the basic inequity which could never be righted: not that the male had a wonderful added attraction called a penis, but that the female had a wonderful all-weather cunt. Neither storm nor sleet nor dark of night could faze it. It was always there, always ready. Quite terrifying, when you think about it. No wonder men hated women. No wonder they invented the myth of female inadequacy.*

Male impotence is approached by Erica Jong with a very sharp tongue and without humour. As a man it does not make you any happier. But that is probably not the intention anyway. Apart from

190 Mels van Driel

this, it is striking that this feminist refers to the female sexual organ linguistically as male. According to the Dutch dictionary, this is allowed, but it is not very appropriate.

As mentioned above, taking the initiative in a sexual context is no longer a male prerogative. Women make demands nowadays that the partner has to meet, or face the punishment of being replaced. Some direct their partner as a football coach: stroke me left a bit, a bit harder, a bit more softly, etc.. In the past, the man prescribed what happened in bed, and the women endured it more or less. Currently, a woman will not put up with it if her partner ejaculates within five minutes and subsequently roles over.

According to some experts, the demands made by a woman lead to ambivalence and uncertainty regarding identity. This leads to sexual frustrations, which are expressed for example in the form of 'new impotence'. In her book *Quick Work* Renate Dorrestein adopts a breezy tone about this 'new impotence':

For years and years, my (girl)friends and I had nothing else for it but to brush-up and rebuild our men with our own hands. That that was always easy, I am alas unable to maintain [...]The improvements that we suggested have made many a man grab angrily for his socks before the deed has been done. Ah well, men and the groins - a more fragile issue does not exist.

Dorrestein then further pursues 'new impotence'. 'Little emancipated women were supposed to completely upset their partners. Just lie down and keep your mouth shut, was not how it went any more. Normal, healthy Dutch guys naturally could not take that. They went into a complete decline. All the fault of feminism'. A little further on in the story she is scornful about the fact that all too few men realise that in bed it does not revolve around one person, but around two.

Ultimately, Dorrestein notices that all the stories about 'new impotence' proved to be wrong. 'She has spent much feminist thought on it for nothing'. It appeared that the muttering lovers who had so many worries in relation with women taking the initiative, did not become impotent. On the contrary, they found it more arousing than ever between the sheets! And all that thanks to women's liberation. Nevertheless it remains an unsolved problem that according to influential sexologists, a large number of men do not really like it all that much if their girlfriend lies on top during sex! Apparently, male sexual liberation has only just started.

The cold shoulder

There are no two ways about it that some women give impotent men the cold shoulder. There are also some men who would rather sleep than have sex. Guy de Maupassant draws attention to both imperfections in his story 'A Cock Crowed'. A certain lady, Berthe d'Avancelles is more or less being worshipped by the unmarried baron Joseph de Croissard. Specially for her he organizes parties and shooting-parties at his castle in Normandy. Berthe's husband does not notice a thing. People believe that they live apart owing to 'a certain physical incapacity' that she cannot forgive him. This husband is a short and bald little man with short arms and legs, a short neck, a pug nose, etc., everything about him is short. Berthe in contrast, is a tall, determined, young brunette who laughs at her husband and calls him 'little miss stay-at-home' in the presence of others. In the meantime with a certain amount of pleasure, she lets her tender glance fall upon the broad shoulders, the sturdy frame and the blond moustache of her devoted admirer, baron Joseph de Croissard, with whom she for that matter has not yet been to bed.

One autumn day, another shooting-party has been organised and Berthe is invited. The evening before, Berthe promises the baron that if he is successful at the shoot 'she will give him something'. At the end of the next day, in which the baron has managed to shoot a few wild boar, Berthe d'Avancelles invites the baron to accompany her on a walk through the castle grounds:

With out saying a word and with trembling limbs, he offered her his arm and guided her along with him. As soon as they were alone, they fell into each other's arms. Slowly, with very small steps, they wandered further beneath the almost bare branches through which the moonlight filtered. And their love, their desire to embrace one another became so powerful that they nearly threw themselves down at the foot of a tree.

The sound of hunting horns had died away. The exhausted dogs were asleep in the kennels. 'Let's go inside', said the young woman. They walked back.

When they reached the front of the castle, she murmured with a quite voice, 'I am so tired, I am going to bed, dear friend'.

And when he spread his arms for a last kiss, she hurried away and called back as a farewell, 'No, I am going to bed. He who holds me dear, will follow!'

An hour later, when the whole castle seemed deserted, the baron slipped out of his room on his toes and knocked softly on his beloved's door. When he did not receive an answer, he tried to open it and found that it was not locked.

She was leaning on her elbows, looking out of the window.

He fell to his knees and started to kiss her passionately through her thin nightgown. She said nothing, but ruffled her graceful fingers caressingly through the baron's hair.

Suddenly she broke away from him as if she had made an important decision and said softly in her provoking manner, 'I will return, wait for me.'

And she pointed to a white, vague shape at the back of the dim room: the bed.

Outside himself with excitement, he undressed with shaking fingers, found his way to the bed by touch and slipped quietly between the cool sheets. With a feeling of contentment, he stretched out and was enjoying the caressing brush of the sheets against his tired body so much, that it almost made him forget his lady love.

She still had not returned by the way and apparently found it fun to have him wait a while longer. With a blissful feeling, he closed his eyes and drifted off into a dream, waiting for the delightful things that he had wanted for so long.

But little by little, his limbs became heavy, his thoughts became confused and vague and he dropped into a doze. Overwhelming fatigue felled him; he was asleep.

He slept the heavy sleep, the irresistible sleep of the exhausted hunter. He slept on until the first light of dawn.

Suddenly, through the still half-open window, a cockerel crowed from the branch of a tree close by. Surprised by the penetrating sound, the baron's eyes fluttered open.

He felt a woman's body against him and was lying in a bed that he did not recognise; in his confusion he forgot everything and stuttered drowsily, 'What? Where am I? What was that?'

Then she answered, she who had not slept a wink all night, with a glance at the man with his tousled hair, his blood-shot eyes and his lips that were still thick with sleep, in the same haughty voice that she used for her husband, 'It was nothing. Just a cock's crow. Go back to sleep again, sir, it doesn't have anything to do with you.'

In the stories by Guy de Maupassant the hunt is often used as a metaphor for the conquest of a woman. And in agreement with real life, this also involves loss of libido and impotence.

If he does not feel like it

According to recent American research, almost 40% of the men had little interest in sex and 30% considered sex with their partner to be a chore, more like work than a game. It was not by accident that a short while later, the first self-help book about this delicate subject appeared in the United States. 'Making sure that you are well rested before you start' plays a very important role. But that is easier said than done. Careers need to be pursued, the mortgage has to be paid, etc.. That is already tiring enough.

It is also possible that the man no longer feels like it because his wife has received promotion and not only earns more money, but also has long working hours, which means that he has to 'step in' at home. Or the man might no longer want to because 'it' has to happen every Saturday night. And then he is tired. Logical don't you think, after such a full week and entertaining guests on Saturday evening, while the next morning he has to be up early to go jogging with the neighbour?

The enlightened Dutch feminist Yvonne Kroonenberg explained why the postmodern man sometimes does not feel like it in her book *You Can Get Used to Anything Except a Man*. In her opinion it is a very good question whether men are really so sexually orientated or whether they just claim to be so. She knows a great many women who complain about the opposite. She tells a story about Anke. She is married to Henk, a sturdy and pleasant fellow who prefers to be at his computer than at Anke. They had consulted doctors, expert sexologists, who suspected that Henk has obscure sexual inhibitions. But Henk had shrugged his shoulders and said:

> *An orgasm is nice, but it's such a fuss to get that far. I don't find it much fun to just lie on top of Anke and bang away, so first we have to make it cosy, then I want to stroke her and make sure that she comes. It is not until after that that I want to screw her and its not decent behaviour to go straight to sleep afterwards, so we make love a little more. Its all really good fun, but not something for every day.*

Another man told that he suffers badly from 'objectivity'. When he is busy with a woman, he sees himself in the act. He sees his white buttocks going up and down and is always embarrassed to death. That is why he would rather do nothing!

Apparently there are quite a few men who do not always feel like it. Modern women must learn to accept that. A man is not a machine. So many demands are made on him these days: at work, in the upbringing, at the stove, and to cap it all, also in bed!

5
Erection, Art and Science

Erection, orgasm and reproduction form part of a long cycle, in which people transmit their lives to their offspring. After all, we not only exist for ourselves, but also for our ancestors and our progeny.

In this respect, a special meaning has been attributed to erection. According to Georges Bataille, one of the first members of the surrealistic movement, the whole journey that humankind has made, from one-cell micro-organism to homo sapiens erectus, is an erection in itself. Nevertheless he believes that this erection is imperfect, because human eyes still lie parallel to the earth and humans are still unable to bear the sight of their ultimate goal, the blinding sun.

Bataille was obsessed with atheism, eroticism and mysticism. He occupied himself with psychoanalysis, economics, philosophy and sociology. He wrote poetry, novels and studies on ethnology, visual arts and literature. And always, God, sex and death formed his themes. In *Visions of Excess* Bataille explains that humankind will have achieved its goal when the pineal gland in the frontal lobes of the brain, bursts open and the contents of the human body stream out, in ejaculatory spurts, in the direction of the sun: the logical conclusion of human evolution.

The connection that Bataille makes between the sun and sexuality is not completely ridiculous. When the days become longer in the spring, and trees and shrubs blossom, many hearts respond in kind. The sun has a special affect on the brain. The production of melatonin - a hormone that inhibits sexuality - decreases as the sun shines longer.

Sexologists

The first sexologists were strongly influenced by Victorian reasoning. Havelock Ellis (1859-1939), an English doctor, was the first Victorian to hold modern views on sexuality. In his opinion, a person's attitude towards sexuality is determined individually and culturally. This was something completely new, because in the preceding centuries, sex was considered to be the same for all people.

The contribution made by Sigmund Freud (1856-1939) is well-known. He gave the subconscious a name and gave names to the sexual components of our personality. Freud was one of the first doctors to *listen* to his patients. He was the first to point out how important it is for the patient himself to gain insight into his own problems.

Theodoor Hendrik van de Velde (1873-1937), a Dutch gynaecologist, also made an important contribution to sexology. His book *The Perfect Marriage* published in 1926 was the most famous of all sex education books. More than one million copies were sold. He emphasized the importance of the sexual relationship. Unfortunately he spoilt the sexual practise of his readers by propagating that they always had to try to achieve simultaneous orgasm - a far too romantic conception of the matter. In this respect, some sex education books do more harm than good.

In America it was Dickinson (1861-1950) who did pioneering work, also on women. For example, he examined the vagina using a hollow glass tube in the form of a penis with a lamp shining through. In this way he could directly observe the inside of the vagina. This instrument was refined by later researchers.

Alfred Kinsey (1894-1956) who was originally a biologist, chiefly performed quantitative research into human sexuality. Obviously many 'case reports' had been published, particularly by Freudians, but no one had conducted large surveys. Certain types of sexual behaviour that are nowadays considered to be perfectly normal, were considered to be abnormal by Freudians. Kinsey made it clear that a great deal of 'abnormal' sexual behaviour is completely normal, for example homosexuality.

William Masters and Virginia Johnson were the founders of modern sexology, a typical interdisciplinary science. They dared to observe and measure sexual reactions in the same way that physiologists had studied respiration and digestion. Right from the very beginning of his scientific work, Masters decided to work with at least one woman, because as a man he could never properly understand how a woman experiences sexuality. That was a gilded thought. The same might also apply to the treatment of men with erectile problems. Only men can really understand what an impotent man feels.

Masters and Johnson immediately became famous when they published their first book *Human Sexual Inadequacy* in 1966. *Time* magazine wrote: Older couples will be able to enjoy a healthy and normal sex life for much longer than before, certainly until well into their eighties. This sort of praise was a typical reaction of the mass media. Masters and Johnson wrote the following about impotence:

At every sexual contact, there is immediate overwhelming concern about whether or not he will be able to get an erection. Will he be able to do 'it' like any normal man? He is continuously occupied not only with getting an erection, but also with maintaining one that is adequate enough to copulate with. In simple terms: his concern stands in the way of his getting an erection in the normal way. Many men who are suffering from anxiety in relation to their sexual functioning have distorted this fundamental natural response so much, that they literally break into a sweat every time the opportunity of sexual contact arises.

Another meaningful paragraph:

The cultural principle that the male partner has to accept that he is totally responsible for achieving a successful coitus relationship, places a psychological burden on the shoulders of every man during coitus and has freed the woman from even the slightest suggestion that she is just as much responsible for the success of coitus.

Masters and Johnson put forward the idea that if the husband is impotent, then the couple should make more time for each other, for example two evenings per week. On one of the evenings the husband should create the correct atmosphere and on the other evening, the wife, preferably with music and nice things to eat, such as crisps, raw carrots and cauliflower in sauce. And then it was the idea that the couple lay naked on the sofa and stroked each other. The man had to keep his hands 'above the belt'! The intention was to remove sexuality from the atmosphere of numbness, pressure-to-succeed and fear-of-failure.

In a number of cases the therapy appeared to be effective. This might have something to do with what we used to call 'touching home' during a game of hide-and-seek. If you were standing or sitting in a certain place you could not be caught. Some women appreciated 'touching home', because according to the exercise they could not be grabbed below the belt. Instead they could have their back rubbed and such like - actually very primitive, but sometimes it worked.

If that did not work, couples could receive therapy from Masters and Johnson at the clinic. In order to treat single impotent men, they had recruited a number of female volunteers. These had been selected very carefully. During therapy, the three main aims were: the man had to lose his fear-of-failure, and break the habit of playing the role of spectator and the woman had to regain confidence in her partner. These goals had to be achieved by means of touch-concentration exercises. Just like at home, the partners were not permitted to have coitus in the initial phase. They were only allowed to stroke each other, etc.. Therefore they did not have to worry about failure.

In the majority of cases, the man got an erection after only one or two sessions. At that stage, the couple still did not receive permission to have coitus. They had to continue to pleasure each other by stroking, until the erections kept occurring regularly. Then the couple had to practice losing the erection and regaining it. The idea was that the man overcame his fear that his erection would wilt during coitus and that he would not get another one. When the experts considered that the time had come for the man to make an attempt to enter the vagina, the woman was instructed to kneel on top of the man. She had to help the penis into her vagina and at this stage, not make any demands at all. If the erection wilted, she had to encourage a new one with her hand. This treatment proved to be successful in more than 60% of the men.

The treatment method received the necessary criticism. One objection was that the human aspects of sexual intercourse were disregarded. According to the critics, Masters and Johnson saw coitus far too much as a sort of mechanical process of stimulation and reactions to it. They were considered to be neglecting the psychological elements of human sexual experiences. Despite all the criticism, these two scientists are regarded as the founders of modern sexology.

In 1995 the Dutch psychologist Erick Janssen made a major contribution to scientific research into erectile problems. He made a distinction between the *reflex* erection and the random *psychogenic* erection. The former is seated in the spinal cord and is the result of touching or stimulating the penis, while the latter originates in the brain as a reaction to visual impulses or erotic fantasies. Very little research had been conducted into how they combine and interact. Janssen designed a project in which interaction could be studied. Impotent volunteers were exposed to physical and visual erotic stimuli, separately or in combination. Physical stimuli were provided by a circular vibrator placed around the penis, while visual stimuli comprised erotic film fragments.

If a man's impotence probably had a psychological cause, established in the old-fashioned way, Janssen found that the purely physical stimulation with the vibrator hardly ever led to an erection. When these men were also watching an erotic film, it was far easier for them to get an erection - as if their anxiety about their own sexual functioning was chiefly affecting the 'reflex erection'. Apparently, the erotic film suppressed these worries and the physical experience - the vibrator against the penis - was placed in a more sexual context.

Negative experiences or sexual anxiety can impede a man's erectile capacity. Janssen also found evidence to support this. If, while the impotent men were watching an erotic film, they were asked to do some mental arithmetic or to watch a Tom and Jerry cartoon, the existing erection became stronger, as if these circumstances banished any negative sexual thoughts from their heads. Mental arithmetic and cartoon mice can evidently help to counteract impotence!

Furthermore, according to Janssen, fear of failure is not usually a cause of impotence, which is in contrast with what is generally believed. Research has shown that this theory is not always correct. For example, a number of volunteers were asked to get an erection within two minutes, otherwise they would receive an electric shock. 'We never actually gave any electric shocks', said Janssen, 'but the threat did increase the level of sexual arousal. And when you go to bed with someone for the first time, it would not work according to the theory. But at that moment you are only thinking of one thing and in the majority of cases, all is well'.

Several years ago, the well-known professor of sexology, Koos Slob, from Rotterdam, aired his views about modern diagnostic techniques in a newspaper interview entitled: *Good conversation and sex films against erectile problems:*

> *Modern diagnostic techniques are so sensitive that if you or I went to a urologist, he or she would always find something or other physically wrong with us. But whether or not that abnormality will also lead to problems, is very much the question.*

The interviewer continued by saying that Slob no longer took his car for a major overhaul, but just had the essentials looked at, such as the tyres and brakes. Slightly later he allowed the professor to say:

There can be no two ways about it. Physical causes are overrated. In my opinion, far too many and far too expensive tests are performed on men with erectile problems. A fairly simple test with an extensive questionnaire, a 10-minute erotic film and sleeping for a few nights wearing a piece of [measuring] tape around the penis, would save a great deal of medical expense. This approach makes a direct association between sex and eroticism, and many urologists tremble at the thought.

Not only in the interview, but also in his oration: The physiology and pathophysiology of sexuality, the professor emphasized his opinion that in the majority of men with erectile problems, the cause is psychological. Between his ears, in other words! Occasionally he does see some good in a 'minor urological overhaul'. At this point it is important to mention that it is a serious misconception by the professor from Rotterdam that urologists tremble at the thought of making a direct association between the penis, sex and eroticism. Within urology, the psychosomatic aspects are receiving more and more attention. In general, it can be said that particularly in a strict scientific sense, more interest is being shown in the influence of the psyche - call it the brain - on individual organs. A typical example is the development of neurocardiology.

In his inaugural speech, Slob presented a meaningful motto:

We never think about how soft our penis is. All the same, it is just as well that the majority of men have a soft one most of the time. We undervalue our genital softness not only because we adopt so many phallic values in the patriarchate, but also because we all identify masculine energy and real masculinity with the vitality of a youthful male charisma. As we grow older, our erections gradually become softer. Afraid as we are of our own mortality, we do not want to see our own genital softness, but instead project this characteristic at women who we find weak, and soft and vulnerable - all signs of mortality, all characteristics that we look down upon and deny having.[...]

Undervaluation of genital softness and overvaluation of the phallus have made the world a dangerous place for men. The price we have to pay for this undervaluation is the loss of essential spiritual energy and might. This is the energy and might that are associated with the 'Via Negativa'.

Naturally, this motto that originated from Nelson, contains some charming sentences, but in the everyday practise of impotence treatment, a urologist will not get very far by talking like that. Slob realises this, too. Nevertheless the opinions of urologists and psychologists continue to differ. A famous sexologically-orientated professor of psychology not so long ago qualified urological intervention with impotence as 'plumber's work.' However, he forgot - and we may excuse him for this because he is not a doctor - that urologists are known everywhere as the most intelligent of all surgical specialists. In other words, they are clever plumbers. They earn their living with it, perhaps that is the problem?

You get the picture? Psychiatrists, psychologists and sexologists do not like to have the bread taken out of their mouths! For almost one hundred years these behavioural experts have helped to make sure that fundamental research into the physical causes for impotence did not get off the ground. After all, impotence nearly always has a psychological cause. This attitude led to therapeutic nihilism and did not encourage doctors to perform further examinations ('You're not twenty years old any more, you know').

When the first men walked on the moon, our knowledge of the mechanism of erection did not reach any further than that there were 'cushions' within the cavernous bodies of the penis that could retain blood. Fortunately, a great deal of research has been performed over the past twenty years. Much has been redeemed. All sorts of refined methods have been and are being tested: the pharmaco-erection, visual sexual stimulation, hormone tests, duplex scanning, nightly erection measurements, selective arteriography, dynamic cavernography, etc.. However, the value of these examination techniques in everyday practise has never really been established. The same also applies to the results of new treatment methods. Urologists are expected to be modest. In general, urological findings only reflect a very limited part of the everyday, sometimes oh so bitter, truth. Writers, great and small, men and women, without doubt have a broader, more human view of reality. William Shakespeare warned us of the dangers of excessive alcohol consumption, Jean-Jacques Rousseau made it clear that a sexual encounter with a 'courtesan' is not all that it is made out to be, while Johann Wolfgang von Goethe warned us about having a bit on the side, Guy de Maupassant emphasized the importance of relaxed love-making, Cesare Pavese drew attention to the alarming nature of congenital abnormalities, Willem Frederik Hermans brought up the use of aphrodisiacs, John Irving and Jan Wolkers described impotence caused by penile injury and Hans Plomp did not deny that sometimes, a man - fortunately usually only in his dreams - can behave like a brute.

And what do we find? Impotence and other penile abnormalities do not hurt as much if writers include them in their work. In this way, reading changes into a mental operation. 'Suffering' is placed in a broader context. This is one of the functions of the literature, also in this respect.

Future developments

To be able to offer men with erectile problems the best possible help, urologists will have to be prepared to continue to work with sexologists. If a case presents itself, general practitioners should refer patients primarily to sexologists or urologists trained in sexology. Thanks to the efforts of the International Society for Impotence Research, many hospitals have impotence teams, in which different specialists work in fruitful cooperation. This will undoubtedly lead to improvements in care.

If impotence and other sexual complaints, such as premature ejaculation, are viewed purely as physical abnormalities, then we run the risk of medicalising sexology. In addition, there is the danger of further standardisation, perfectionism, mechanisation and dehumanisation of sexual relationships. It is obviously not a question of whether is it possible to influence sexual desire, erection, ejaculation, orgasmic feelings, etc.. Of course we can! If mankind has managed to send a manned space craft safely to the moon and back, then we can also develop medication or equipment to speed up, slow down, intensify, stimulate or decrease libido, erection, ejaculation or orgasm, according to our wishes. It is not a question of how we can introduce more technology into sexuality. Erection pacemakers have been available for several years. The question is, what do people want to do with sexuality!

Where will further medicalisation of sexuality lead? The past twenty years have seen explosive developments. One could ask whether all the time, effort and money have been well-spent. Is mutual sexual satisfaction well-served by equipment, pills or operations? Isn't sex usually something that two people do together? Very little sexological research has been performed into the results of modern treatment techniques.

Some sexologists, not surprisingly, are sickened by the fact that so much attention is paid to the phallus. Despite all the short-comings of sex therapy, it does at least lay some degree of emphasis on mutual pleasure, communication and creativity; and both men and women are invited to participate. Neither the man nor the woman is excluded, nor kept in the dark.

Obviously some women will find more enjoyment in harder and more long-lasting erections; and some women will benefit more if their partner is no longer weighed down by fear of failure and has regained sufficient self-confidence to be able to have sex 'normally'.

There will, of course, also be women who are not happy about an artificial erection. Hard and long-lasting erections are not automatically a blessing for humanity! Many women will probably not be pleased with the idea of frequent confrontations with a stiff penis when they are in their seventies or eighties. Female sexologists have very good reason to point out carefully that the vagina of a postmenopausal woman does not usually become moist, in other words, is no longer meant to be penetrated.

For every pound spent on artificial erections, why not save one to spend on the women. Give women the chance to air their complaints about men. Complaints about their lack of tenderness, about their inadequate attempts at communication, about their often inadequate personal hygiene and about their lacking insight into eroticism. There are still so many men who cannot dance without treading on their partner's toes, who do not take the trouble to write a love poem and refuse to learn how to massage the clitoris in such a way that it is pleasurable. How many men are too selfish to get out of bed at night to change the baby's nappy so that the mother can have an uninterrupted night's sleep? It is time they started to realise that for many women, the most enjoyable foreplay of all is being helped with the washing-up.

But the men should not let the women walk all over them. Men should not become 'soft'. Such men used to be called softies or suckers and such names do not befit a man. A man is and should remain a sort of bull. However, men who time and time again 'mount' their partner like a bull, should no longer be tolerated in enlightened Europe. A mechanical approach is the biggest turn-off for women. She will feel that she is being treated like a machine or a (rubber) doll, or like something to be licked, stroked or sucked, depending on what her partner has seen recently on the television. No emotional communication, no fun, just pure calculation to get the job done as effectively as possible.

The fundamental problem is not so much male impotence, as the sexual relationship. Nowadays many men are not satisfied with their lives. In this situation we must be careful that erection and coitus do not become the ultimate goals of sexuality. Only investing in seeking the perfect erection or perfect coitus would not be wise.

Perhaps the solution for impotence should be sought in setting up a national network of self-help groups, such as that in America under the name Impotents Anonymous. As the name suggests, impotence sufferers compare themselves to a certain extent with alcoholics. The network was set up in 1982 by The Impotence Institute of America, created by the millionaire Bruce MacKenzie, who after many years of psychotherapeutic treatment, ultimately regained his happiness in life thanks to an erection prosthesis. It is understandable that only urologists are appointed to the board of directors at his institute. MacKenzie and his wife wrote the book *It is not all in your head*, which found wide and enthusiastic readership.

In Holland, some special clinics offer group therapy. This sexological treatment is chiefly aimed at men who do not have a steady partner. Such a group comprises five to seven men, who get together once a week for about twenty weeks, under the supervision of a sexologist. During the sessions, a great deal of attention is paid to all sorts of sexual myths, for example that a man should always be capable of having coitus.

The interested reader will be delighted to know that there is a quarterly magazine about the penis, called *Penis Power Quarterly*. The magazine is not for the medical profession, but for the layman.

To conclude

One thing is certain: sexuality, including sexual potency, is the great motor of nature. Reproduction forms the basis of our existence. You cannot get away from this, nor can you deny it. It is important not only to have respect for sexuality, but also for the problems of an impotent man. Many people are unable to manage this. Hatred towards men who cannot use their genital organ for the full one hundred per cent, has existed since the beginning of time. Apparently, little can be done about this situation, just as little as about impotence itself, because the complaint cannot always be put right.

Growing older means an unpleasant physical decline. That will never change. However, we live in a society in which a healthy, vigorous, young, beautiful and potent body has been elevated to measuring-rod status. In fact, the ideal view of the body as 'a machine that must function well for ever and ever' is based on suppression, not only by present-day *Young One - culture*, but also by ourselves. Suppression of the undeniable reality that every single one of us lives in a body that is mortal, that can let us down, that can become ill, and that one day will die. Consequently, it will often be a great relief for a man to be able to talk freely about his feelings of impotence, fear of failure or apparent resignation. Not only resignation about his impotence, but also about death. People realised this early on; in 1810 Smit wrote:

> *Secret and openly-pronounced complaints about male weaknesses are now more numerous that ever before. To indicate to the man, as well as to the woman, the sickly condition that contains the causes for the impotence, to teach them ways to deal with these causes, if not to lift them completely, then to decrease them, to make them competent in procreation, in recognising homely and marital happiness, is, for the Doctor, for the friend of humankind, a not unimportant obligation.*

Becoming old and impotent, as I have tried to explain, cannot really be influenced. Obviously, it is possible to camouflage old-age and impotence with gadgets which according to some women, through their deceptiveness and their despicability, are the accomplices of a desperate man who will stop at nothing. False teeth, a toupee or wig, false coronary arteries, a false pill - prick - pump - or prosthesis erection - sometimes it is too depressing to talk about. Naturally, this is also valid for face-lifts, fat-removal operations, etc.. And doesn't dying your hair with henna, which is common practice among forty-year-old women whose hair is greying, also form part of the battle (that has already been lost) against decline and death?

Besides the above-mentioned reproductive function, we people can confirm the 'feeling of togetherness' by means of sex. Sexual contact can revitalise and offer relief against stress. It is a great form of relaxation and recreation. Moreover, sex is a good 'sleeping pill'. Whether we experience this in practise, is another matter. More than we realise, our experience of sex is also associated with being consciously or unconsciously occupied with the goal of our existence, with being satisfied or dissatisfied with the role we have in life, and with the love that we feel or do not feel around us. More than we realise, our sexual behaviour also obeys dark powers that we are not really aware of.

The Mexican poet, essayist and Nobel prize winner, Octavio Paz, described in *The Double Flame* how in his opinion sexuality, eroticism and love are interrelated. He feels that the red part of the flame symbolises the primal instinct of sexuality, which we share with animals. More towards the centre, the flame is yellow. This points to the element of play in eroticism, which gives sexuality a human tint in every culture. The inner part of the flame is transparent blue. There sexuality and eroticism have been purified into the pre-eminently human capability to love. Perhaps it would help if care providers tried to keep this model in mind a bit more.

According to Paz, eroticism can free itself from sexuality. Flames change, they flicker. Eroticism causes sexuality to deviate from its evolutionary goal: reproduction. But the changes, the deviations, are paradoxically enough, also a turning back. The human pair making love, return to the genital sea and rock themselves on the endless, calm swell. There they regain the innocence of wild animals. 'Eroticism is a rhythm: one of her chords is parting, the other is revolving, returning to placative nature. The erotic hereafter is here and now. Every woman and every man has experienced such moments: they are our portion of paradise, said Paz.

Bibliography

Introduction

J.B. Bousquet. *Natuurkundige beschouwing van het huwelijk in betrekking tot de maatschappelijke zedelijkheid, de bevolking en de gezondheid.* 's Gravenhage: K. Fuhri, 1842.

A.C. Kinsey, W.B. Pomeroy, C.E. Martin. *Sexual behaviour in the male.* Philadelphia: Saunders, 1948.

About The Secret Part

Anoniem. Discussie over penislengte in Europees Parlement. *De Gay Krant* - 30 oktober 1993.

E. Belt. 'Leonardo the Florentine'. *Investigative Urology* 1965; 3:1.

J.C. Blonk. *Koro. Geneeskundig Tijdschrift voor Nederlands-Indië* 1895; 35: 150-168.

E. Bootsma. We zijn gewoon te klein. *De Gay Krant*, 13 mei 1995.

The Holy Bible. Translated out of the original tongues: and with the former translations diligently compared and revised, by his majesty's special command. London: CUP, 1972.

S.M. Bierman. 'The peripatetic posthumous peregrination of Napoleon's penis'. *The Journal of Sex Research* 1992; 29: 579-580.

A. Bijlsma. 'Penisomtrek en condooms'. *SOA bulletin* 1995; 15: 26-27.

P. Canaponi. *Een gondel in de Herengracht en andere verhalen.* *Querido*: Amsterdam, 1978.

B. McCarthy. *Sexual awareness, a practical approach.* San Francisco: Boyd & Fraser, 1975.

H. Claus. *Het jaar van de kreeft.* Amsterdam: De Bezige Bij, 1984.

D. Courtade. *Notions practiques d'électrothérapie appliquée à l'urologie.* Paris, 1921.

M. Dekkers. *Lief dier.* Amsterdam: Contact, 1992.

C. Eckhardt. 'Untersuchungen über die Erektion des Penis beim Hund'. *Beitragen Anatomie und Physiologie* 1863; 3: 123.

H. Eliott. *On penises.* Boston: University Press, 1967.

K.W. Feldman, D.W. Smith. 'Fetal phallic growth and penile standards for new born male infants'. *The Journal of Pediatrics* 1975; 86: 395.

W. Fisher, N. Branscombe, Ch. Lemery. 'The bigger the better? Arousal and attributional responses to erotic stimuli that depict different size penises'. *Journal of Sex Research* 1983; 19: 377.

R. Giphart. *Giph.* Amsterdam: Nijgh & van Ditmar, 1993.

R. de Graaf. *Virorum organis inservientibus, de clysteribus et usu siphonus in anatomia.* Roterodamensis: Ex Officina Hackiana, 1668.

G. Griffin. *Penis Enlargement Methods - Fact & Phallusy.* Ninth Edition. Palm Springs: Added Dimensions Publishing, 1996.

D. de Groot. Binnenkort ook in Europa penisvergrotende operaties. *De Gay Krant,* 18 september 1993.

W.A. Hammond. *Sexual impotence in the male*. New York: Birmingham & Co, 1883.

R.M. Hawley, J.H. Owens. 'Koro: its presentation in an elderly male'. *International Journal of Geriatric Psychiatry* 1988; 3: 69-72.

A.F.Th. van der Heijden. *De sandwich*. Amsterdam: Querido, 1986.

H.F.J. Horstmanshof & H. Beukers. 'Viriel - de namen voor het membrum virile'. *Tijdschrift voor de geschiedenis van de geneeskunde*, september 1995.

E. Kamvisseli. f/32: *The second coming*. London: Virago Press, 1993.

P. de Kruif. *The male hormone*. New York: Harcourt Brace, 1945.

D.H. Lawrence. *Lady Chatterly's Lover*. Amsterdam: Bert Bakker, 1977.

V.D. Lespinasse. Impotence: its treatment by transplantation of testicle. Surgical Clinics of Chicago 1918; 2: 281.

H. Loeb. 'Harnröhrenkapazität und Tripperspritzen'. *Münchener Medizinische Wochenschrift* 1899; 46: 1019.

Ch. Malinick, J.A. Flaherty, Th. Jobe. 'Koro: how culturally specific?' *International Journal of Social Psychiatry* 1985; 31: 67.

J. de Man. De groene fee. *HP/De Tijd*, 20 januari 1995 (over Paul Verlaine).

A. Moravia. *The two of us*. London: Martin Secker & Warburg Limited, 1972.

P.T. Mountjoy. 'Some early attempts to modify penile erection in horse and human: an historical analysis'. *The Psychological Record* 1974; 24: 291-308.

The Kama Sutra of Vatsyayana. Translated by Sir Richard Burton and F.F. Arbuthnot. London: George Allen and Unwin Ltd, 1963.

R. Nijland. 'In twee uur is de penis dubbel zo lang'. *De Volkskrant*,

20 augustus 1994.

H. Overganck. *De Tooverstaf.* Oosterbeek: Schartens, 1939.

R. Payne Knight and Th. Wright. *A history of phallic worship.* New York: Dorsett Press, 1992.

G.F. Poggio. *Liber Facetiarum.* cited in: *De Volkskrant,* 29 amr 996.

S.A. Piesol. *Human anatomy.* Philadelphia: Lippincott, 1907.

J. Ponce de León, F. Algaba, J. Salvador. 'Cutaneous horn of glans penis'. *British Journal of Urology* 1994; 74: 257.

P. Roobjee. *De kleinzoon van de letterzetter.* Leuven: Uitgeverij van Halewyck, 1995.

F. Sagan. *Als een verre glimlach.* Antwerpen/Amsterdam: Manteau, 1978.

R. Schouten. *Met de hand. Bevredigende gedichten.* Amsterdam: De Arbeiderspers, 1992.

G.R. Scott. *Phallic Worship.* Westport: Menthal Health Press, 1956.

J. van der Spek. 'Therapie bij impotentia coëundie'. *Medisch Weekblad voor Noord-en Zuid-Nederland* 1898; 5: 14.

K. Siminoski, J. Bain. 'The relationship among heigth, penile length and foot size'. *Annals of Sex Research* 1993; 6: 231-235.

E. Steinach & J. Loebel. *Sex and life.* London: Faber & Faber, 1939.

H. van Straten. *Razernij der liefde. Ontuchtige poëzie in de Nederlanden van Middeleeuwen tot Franse Tijd.* Amsterdam: De Arbeiderspers, 1992.

P. Thomas. *Kama Kalpa or The Hindu Ritual of Love.* Bombay: Taraporevala Sons & Co, 1959.

R. Tullii, R. Ferreira, C. Guillaux, N. Pangratis. 'Evaluation of neurotomy in primary premature ejaculation patients'. *International*

Journal of Impotence Research 1995; 7: 81.

S. Voronoff. *Testicular grafting from ape to man.* Translated by Theodore Merrill. Brentano Ltd, 1930.

L. de Vries. *Ha dokter Ho dokter, knotsgekke geneeskunde uit grootvaders tijd.* Haarlem: De Haan, 1976.

P. Vroon, A. van Amerongen en H. de Vries. *Verborgen verleider. Psychologie van de reuk.* Baarn: Ambo, 1994.

J. van der Vuurst de Vries. *Over impotentie en hare behandeling.* Baarn: Hollandia Drukkerij, 1916.

A H. Walton. The story of testosterone and rejuvenation. In: *Aphrodisiacs: from legend to prescription.* Westport, Connecticut: Associated Booksellers, 1958.

Wen-Shing Tseng, Mo Kan-Ming, Jing Hsu, Li Li Shuen, Ou Li-Wah, Chen Guo-Qian, Jiang Da-Wei. 'A sociocultural study of koro epidemics in Guangdong', China. *American Journal of Psychiatry* 1988; 145: 1538.

Dr. Jacobus X. *Untrodden fields of anthropology.* Paris: Charles Carrington, 1898.

B. Zilbergeld. *Male sexuality.* New York: Bantam, 1978.

Impotence

J.G.R. Acquoy. *Het klooster te Windesheim en zijn invloed. Uitgegeven door het Provinciaal Utrechts Genootschap van Kunsten en Wetenschappen.* Utrecht: van der Post, 1876.

G.E. Beheri. Surgical treatment of impotence. *Plastic & Reconstructive Surgery* 1960; 38: 92.

G. Bernant. 'Sexual behaviour: Hard time with the Coolidge effect'. In: MH Siegel & HP Ziegler (Eds). *Psychological Research: The Inside Story* (pp. 214-237). New York: Harper &

Row, 1976.

W.R. Bett. 'The os penis in man and beast'. *Proceedings of the Royal Society of Medicine* 1951; 44: 433.

N.A. Bogoras. *Über die volle plastische Wiederherstellung eines zum Koitus fähigen Penis.* Zentralblatt Chirurgie 1936; 22: 1271.

G. de Bruijn. *Vrijen met een man, kan dat dan?* Baarn: In den Toren, 1985.

W. Bühl. *Eros met grijzende slapen.* Vertaald door Oscar Timmers. Amsterdam: Wereld-Bibliotheek, 1962.

The Holy Bible. Translated out of the original tongues: and with the former translations diligently compared and revised, by his majesty's special command. London: Cambridge University Press, 1972.

J. Chang. *The tao of love and sex - the ancient Chinese way to ecstasy.* London: Wildwood House Ltd, 1977.

G. Culichia. *Iets heel anders. In: Ciao Bella, Italiaanse verhalen over vrouwen. Onder redactie van Marina Warners.* Amsterdam: Wereldbibliotheek, 1995.

P. Darmon. *Le tribunal de l'impuissance.* Parijs: Editions du Seuil, 1979.

P. Dufour & Fr. Helbing. *Geschiedenis der Sexueele Zeden.* Zalt-Bommel: H.J. van de Garde & Co, 1910.

G. Duvidier. *Gids voor lijders en lijderessen aan ziekten der urine- en geslachtswerktuigen. Aanzienlijk vermeerderd en verbeterd door docter A. Moussaud.* Gouda: Van Goor en Zonen, 1921.

H. Ellis. *Studies in the psychology of sex.* Philadelphia: Davis, 1911.

C. van Emde Boas. *Geschiedenis van de seksuele normen.* Antwerpen: De Nederlandsche Boekhandel, 1985.

C.J.P. Erikson, T. Fukunaga, R. Lindman. 'Sex hormone response to alcohol'. *Nature*, June 30, 1994, p 711.

J. Frenken, K. Rodenburg, B. van Stolk. *Huisartsen helpen bij seksuele moeilijkheden*. Deventer: van Loghum Slaterus, 1988.

J.W. von Goethe. *Sämtliche Werke. Pandora Klassiker. Mit Einleitungen von Paul Ernst, Cäsar Flaischer u.a*. Berlin: Ullstein, 1923.

E.J.K.J.E.M. van Grunsven, F.M.J.A. Froeling, J.D.M. de Vries. Top (termination of pregnancy) of flop? Een sociaal-maatschappelijk en psychoseksuele ontwikkelingsevaluatie bij volwassen patiënten met een exstrophie van de blaas. De Urograaf 1992; 6: 27.

P. Fontana. De agenda. In: Ciao Bella, *Italiaanse verhalen over vrouwen. Onder redactie van Marina Warners*. Amsterdam: Wereldbibliotheek, 1995.

A.F.Th. van der Heijden. *De gevaren-driehoek*. Amsterdam: Querido, 1992.

W.F. Hermans. *Onder professoren*. Amsterdam: De Bezige Bij 1990.

J. Irving. *The World According to Garp*. London: Transworld Publishers Ltd, 1976.

Kama Sutra of Vatsyayana. Translated from the Sanskrit. London: Cosmopoli, 1883.

A.C. Kinsey, W.B. Pomeroy, C.E. Martin. *Sexual Behaviour in the Male*. Philadelphia: Saunders, 1948.

M. Kundera. *Afscheidswals*. Baarn: Agathon-AMBO, 1982.

O.S. Lowsley, E.A. Rueda. 'Further experience with an operation for the cure of certain types of impotence'. *The Journal of the International College of Surgeons* 1953; 19: 69.

G.F. Lydston. 'The surgical treatment of impotence'. *The American Journal of Clinical Medicine* 1908; 15: 1571.

A. Marja. *Reisavontuur. In: Reislust - gedichten.* Amsterdam: De Arbeiderspers, 1957.

G. de Maupassant. *Verzamelde verhalen: Rogers methode. Vertaald door Yanik Teeuwisse,* Anita C. van de Ven e.a. Amsterdam: Loeb, 1988.

H. Miller. *Tropic of Cancer.* Paris: Obelisk Press, 1934.

A. Moll. *Handbuch der Sexualwissenschaften.* Leipzig: Vogel, 1912.

A. Moreschi. *Petite Messe Solenelle van Rossini.* Te beluisteren op de CD "Le Temps des Castrates" uitgebracht door EMI in 1994.

F. Parona. 'Imperfetta erezione del pene per varicosità della vena dorsale: osservazione'. *Giornale Italiano delle Malattie Veneree e deela Pelle* 1873; 14: 71.

C. Pavese. *The Business of Living.* London: Quartet Books Limited, 1980.

O. Paz. *De dubbele vlam.* Amsterdam, Meulenhoff, 1994.

H. Plomp. *Het innerlijk bordeel.* Amsterdam: In De Knipscheer, 1990.

S. Polet. *Droom van de oplichter: werkelijkheid. Drie emblemen - eerste kennismaking.* Amsterdam: De Bezige Bij, 1977.

B. Premsela. *Sexuologie in de praktijk.* Amsterdam: Strengholt, 1940.

G. Reve. *Nader tot u.* Amsterdam: Van Oorschot, 1966.

H. Robbins. *The Betsy.* New York: Simon & Schuster, 1971.

J. Roubaud. *Traité de l'impuissance.* Paris, 1876.

J.J. Rousseau. *Confessions.* London: David Campbell Publishers Ltd, 1992.

G.L. Russell. 'Impotence treated by mechanotherapy'. *Proceedings of the Royal Society of Medicine* 1959; 52: 872.

G. Servadio. *The Story of R.* Translated by Allegra Mostyn-Owen. London: Pan Macmillan Publishers Limited, 1994.

W. Shakespeare. *MacBeth.* In: *The complete works of William Shakespeare.* Edited with a glossary by W.J. Craig. London: Henry Pordes, 1990.

H.E. Sigerist. 'Impotence as a result of witchcraft'. In: *Essays in Biology.* Berkely, California: University Press, 1943.

J. Sprenger & H. Institoris. *Malleus Maleficarum.* New York: Dover Publishing Inc., 1971.

H. van Straten. *Razernij der liefde. Ontuchtige poëzie in de Nederlanden van Middeleeuwen tot Franse Tijd.* Amsterdam: De Arbeiderspers, 1992.

Sushruta Samhita. An english translation based on original sanskrit text. Varanasi (India): The Chowkhamba Sanskrit Series Office, 1963.

S. Unsfeld. *Das Tagebuch Goethes und Rilkes Sieben Gedichte.* Frankfurt am Main: Insel Verlag, 1978.

V.G. Vecki. *The pathology and treatment of sexual impotence.* From the author's second german edition, revised and rewritten. Philadelphia: Saunders, 1899.

R. Virag. 'Intracavernous injection of papaverine for erectile failure'. *Lancet* 1982; 2: 938.

J. Weyer. *De Praestigiis Daemonum.* Libris IV, Capitum XX.

L. de Winter. *Hoffman's honger.* Amsterdam: De Bezige Bij, 1990.

B. de Wit. *Een morbide wil tot weten.* Vrij Nederland/ Boekenbijlage, 29 augustus 1987.

K.P. Wolffenbuttel, M.F. van Driel, W.C.M. Weymar Schultz, H.J.A. Mensink. 'Papaverine bij erectiele dysfunctie: de geschiedenis'. *Tijdschrift voor Seksuologie* 1992; 16: 253.

J. Wolkers. *Turks Fruit.* Amsterdam: Meulenhoff, 1969.

W. Zeegers. *De zonnige zijde van seks; de nawerking van positief beleefde seksualiteit.* Leiden: DSWO Press, 1994.

G.J. van Zessen & Th. Sandfort. *Seksualiteit in Nederland.* Amsterdam: Swets & Zeitlinger, 1991.

Zhisui Li. *Het privé-leven van Mao. Onthuld door zijn lijfarts.* Uit het engels vertaald door Jan Braks, Milko van Gool en Lisanne Teunissen. Amsterdam: Balans, 1995.

B. Zilbergeld. *Male Sexuality.* New York: Bantam, 1978.

Other Penile Disorders

The Holy Bible. Translated out of the original tongues: and with the former translations diligently compared and revised, by his majesty's special command. London: Cambridge University Press, 1972.

H.J. van Dam. *Priapea.* Amsterdam: Polak & van Gennep, 1995.

L.H.A. Drabbe. *De sluier.* Amsterdam: van Kampen, 1906. heruitgave te Antwerpen: Scriptoria, 1977.

R. Giphart. *Het feest der liefde.* Amsterdam: Balans, 1995.

Gebroeders Grimm. *Sprookjes voor kind en gezin.* Rotterdam: Lemniscaat, 1981.

E.A. Gutheil. *The Autobiography of Wilhelm Stekel.* New York: Liveright, 1950.

G. de Maupassant. *Rokken en broeken: Vastgeroest.* Vertaald door Ank van Haaren. Amsterdam: Meulenhoff, 1961.

S. Polet. *Breekwater.* Amsterdam: De Bezige Bij, 1963.

R. van der Rijst. *Beloven en geloven. Kind en Zondag - maandblad voor de geloofsopvoeding in en rond de kerk.* Jaargang 64 nr. 1, 1995, p. 20 e.v.

K. Slob. *Seksuele activiteit van vrouwen en mannen boven 50 jaar.*

In: Het Geriatrie Informatorium. Houten: Bohn & Stafleu & Van Loghum, 1990.

A. Soep. *De besnijdenis - een ethnologische studie.* Amsterdam: G.A. van Oorschot, 1947.

W. Stekel. *Die Impotenz des Mannes.* Berlin & Wien: Urban und Schwarzenberg, 1920.

J. Zwagerman. *Vals licht.* Amsterdam: De Arbeiderspers, 1996.

The Woman And Feminism

J. Cats. *Alle de wercken van den Heere Jacob Cats.* Amsterdam en's Gravenhage II, 166a, 1726.

R. Dorrestein. *Korte metten: Prettig vrijen.* Amsterdam: Contact, 1991.

E. Janssen. *'Provoking penile responses - Activation and inhibition of male genital response'.* Thesis, Universiteit van Amsterdam, Faculteit der Psychologie, 1995.

E. Jong. *Fear of Flying.* London: Martin Secker & Warburg Ltd, 1974.

E. Kamvisseli. f/32: *The Second Coming.* London: Virago Press, 1993.

Y. Kroonenberg. *Alles went behalve een vent: Geen zin.* Amsterdam: Contact, 1992.

A. Manschot. *Steeds vaker heeft zij meer zin dan hij.* Maandblad Opzij, oktober 1992.

G. de Maupassant. *Verzamelde verhalen: Een haan kraaide. Vertaald door Yanik Teeuwisse,* Anita C. van de Ven e.a. Amsterdam: Loeb, 1988.

C. van der Pluym. *Versieren. De Gay-krant,* 1 september 1995.

B. Premsela. *Sexuologie in de praktijk.* Amsterdam: Strengholt,

1940.

J. Smit. *De arts voor gehuwden en ongehuwden - een handboek voor mannen en vrouwen die aan onmagt, onvruchtbaarheid en andere werktuigekijke geslagtsgebreken lijden.* Amsterdam: Hesse, 1810.

N. Venette. *Conjugal love; or, the pleasure of the marriage bed.* London: Garland, 1984.

S. Verroen. De laffe smaak van vanilleseks. *De Volkskrant,* 22 mei 1993.

Erection, Art And Science

G. Bataille. *Visions of excess, selected writings, 1927-1939.* Minneapolis, 1985.

H. Ellis. *Studies over de psychologie der sexen.* Analyse van de sexueele aandrift. Baarn: Hollandia, 1922.

E. Janssen. '*Provoking penile responses - Activation and inhibition of male genital response*'. Thesis, Universiteit van Amsterdam, Faculteit der Psychologie, 1995.

A.C. Kinsey, W.B. Pomeroy, C.E. Martin. *Sexual behaviour in the male.* Philadelphia: Saunders, 1948.

B. & E. MacKenzie. *It is not all in your head.* New York: Dutton, 1988.

W.H. Masters & V.E. Johnson. *Human sexual inadequacy.* London: Churchill, 1970.

O. Paz. *De dubbele vlam.* Amsterdam, Meulenhoff, 1994.

K. Slob. *De potentie van psychofysiologisch onderzoek.* Rede uitgesproken bij de aanvaarding van het ambt van bijzonder hoogleraar in de fysiologie en pathofysiologie van de seksualiteit aan de Erasmus Universiteit te Rotterdam op donderdag 13 februari 1992.

K. Slob. 'Goed gesprek en seksfilm tegen erectieproblemen.'
Interview in de *Volkskrant* van 22 februari 1992.

J. Smit. *De arts voor gehuwden en ongehuwden - een handboek voor mannen en vrouwen die aan onmagt, onvruchtbaarheid en andere* werktuigekijke geslagtsgebreken lijden. Amsterdam, Hesse, 1810.

Th. van de Velde. *Ideal marriage: its physiology and technique.* London: Heinemann, 1928.

Index